The British
Heavy Horse

A fine, well-matched pair of Shires owned by Courage's. Courage Ltd

The British
Heavy Horse

Guy Villiers

BARRIE & JENKINS
COMMUNICA - EUROPA

To R – who suggested this book so long ago, and who
at that time could not have envisaged the amount of midnight
oil that would be consumed.

© Barrie and Jenkins Ltd 1976

First published 1976 by
Barrie and Jenkins Ltd
24 Highbury Crescent, London N5 1RX

Reprinted 1977

ISBN 0 214 20095 7

Printed by litho at The Anchor Press Ltd, Tiptree, Essex

Designed by Grahame Dudley

Acknowledgements

I should like to express my gratitude to all the individuals and companies who have contributed in one way or another to this book. In particular, I am indebted to the secretaries of the breed societies: Mr R. W. Bird, Shire Horse Society; Mr W. J. Woods, Suffolk Horse Society; Mr A. E. Vyse, British Percheron Society; Monsieur B. Pinceloup, *Société Hippique Percheronne de France;* Mr B. A. Roy, secretary/treasurer of the Canadian Percheron Society. My thanks also go out to Mr R. J. Brickell and Mr N. Raynor; Mrs M. E. Dash, secretary of the Southern Counties Heavy Horse Association; Mr D. Gossett, secretary of the Percheron Horse Association of America; Mr R. G. Hooper, treasurer of the Heavy Horse Preservation Society; Mrs S. Wilson, publicity director of the American Shire Horse Breeders Association; and Mr N. L. Behrendt of Maryland Shire Horse Associates.

Many individuals and organisations have kindly supplied photographs: Mr W. A. Jackson, editor of the *Shooting Times and Country Magazine,* who also offered valuable advice; James Buchanan and Co. Ltd; Courage and Co. Ltd; J. R. Parkington and Co; Daniel Thwaites and Co. Ltd; Truman Ltd; Vaux and Associated Breweries Ltd; Watney Mann Ltd; Whitbread and Co. Ltd; Young and Co.'s Brewery Ltd; Mr A. D. Crossman (late of Watney Mann Ltd); Mr R. A. Brown, of the London Harness Horse Parade Society; The Hull Brewery Co. Ltd; Tyne Tees Television; Thames Television; and the Museum of English Rural Life, Reading University.

My thanks are also due to the individual photographers who have captured so eloquently the strength and character of the British heavy horse.

Contents

1.
An Introduction
to the Four Main Breeds

*Taking a short cut home – and no plugs or distributor
to be affected by water!* W. Wilkinson

To many who are not actively concerned with horse breeding, agriculture, ploughing societies, country shows at which horses of all classes compete, or with the major breweries, it may seem that the age of the most majestic of all horses – the British heavy horse – is irrefutably at an end. This, thankfully, is not the case.

At the outset it should, perhaps, be mentioned that Shires are a distinctive breed of heavy horse, and not all heavy horses are Shires. Three other breeds – the Suffolk (sometimes referred to as the Suffolk Punch), the Clydesdale and the Percheron are all individual breeds of heavy horse, bred and used in Britain. Magnificent examples of all four breeds can be seen at horse and agricultural shows throughout the country. A number of breweries employ and exhibit one of the four breeds, entering them at country shows where splendid, well-groomed teams, with coats and brasses gleaming, are often one of the main attractions.

It is probably true to say that these horses are loosely thought of as 'cart' horses, employed for draft purposes in addition to their role in agriculture. Their evolution as farm horses goes back at least 400 years – Suffolks are said to date back to the early part of the sixteenth century, and Camden's *Britannia* gives the date as 1506. Long before this period, in the Bronze Age (about 400–600 BC), farmers manually pulled or pushed the earliest form of crude metal plough, which must have been a back-breaking operation. Gradually, teams of oxen came to be used to lessen the physical demands made upon the farmer. The early ox-ploughs were badly designed and often required up to eight oxen, yoked in four pairs, with a man in front as well as one behind the team. At this time, the horses used on farms were considerably smaller and less powerful than the heavy breeds that had evolved by the sixteenth and seventeenth centuries, and were only used for fairly light work such as harrowing. The invasion of the Saxons between the fifth and seventh centuries is said to have started the trend towards a larger type of agricultural horse. The larger German horses brought over by the invaders were crossed with those indigenous to Britain at that time, which were probably no more than 11 hands in height. The earliest references to the horse being used for heavier agricultural work occur in the twelfth century, but several hundred years passed before the introduction of a really large, powerful type of agricultural horse – the predecessor of the main breeds of heavy horse that are the subject of this book.

The heavy armour worn by soldiers in the fourteenth century created a demand for a large and prodigiously strong battle horse, capable of carrying heavily mailed knights in addition to cumbersome military accoutrements designed to protect both horse and rider. It has been estimated that the weight of armour and rider amounted to approximately 400 lbs! Towards the end of the fourteenth century, a large number of horses from Flanders and Holland were imported into Britain by Richard II, with the aim of increasing the strength and size of British horses. (This had already been done, but on a smaller scale, by Henry II in the mid-twelfth century.) During the early part of the sixteenth century, Henry VIII also influenced the development of a larger, stronger horse, stipulating that stallions used for breeding must be at least 14 hands in height. Even bigger stallions, previously confined to use for military purposes, were later handed over to landowners for breeding on their estates. Mares also had to conform to certain standards when used for breeding.

This early progress towards a larger, more powerful British heavy horse, more closely resembling the bigger continental breeds, was assisted by the importation of horses of Spanish, Arab and Italian blood, which were inter-bred with the continental – British crosses to produce a more active horse and one that was slightly less massive in size. This type of horse was used as a coach horse in the sixteenth and seventeenth centuries. During this period, stud farms were being established for the extensive breeding of the heavy type of horse, both for military requirements and for agricultural purposes, including draft work. Towards the end of the seventeenth century, a heavy breed of dark-coloured horses was introduced into Britain from Holland; these were later described as the English Black Horse, or the Great Horse, a name also given to the large European breeds of the fourteenth and fifteenth centuries. Some distinguished writers claim that these seventeenth-century black horses from Holland were the ancestors of the present-day breed of Shire horse. It is, however, more probable that the earliest origins of the Shire as a distinctive breed lie in the sixteenth century, and result from the crossing of Flemish and Dutch horses with those indigenous to the English shires. In the same way the Scottish Clydesdale also owes a number of its basic characteristics to the introduction into Britain over 250 years ago of more than one European breed of heavy horse.

The evolution of the horse for agricultural use, then, progressed from the much smaller animals of the twelfth century to the breeds of heavy horse that we know today, via the release for stud purposes of the larger and more powerful military horses of the sixteenth century and the influence of the heavier continental breeds imported between the fourteenth and seventeenth centuries, aided by the infusion of Spanish, Arab and Italian blood. This heavy type of draft horse succeeded the much slower and far less amenable ox for farm cultivation and for draft work. The farming work for which they were used included ploughing, harrowing, drilling, rolling, numerous harvesting duties, and pulling heavy loads of sugar beet, mangolds, turnips, grain and hay, while their use as draft animals involved hauling heavy loads on forestry plantations and on the roads.

By the eighteenth century, distinctive breeds of agricultural heavy horse had established themselves, including the Suffolk Punch from East Anglia, the Clydesdale from Scotland and similar horses from several of the midland shires – breeds that have endured, both in Britain and abroad, for over 250 years. One contemporary chronicler calculated that the number of horses of all types employed in agriculture amounted to well over half a million in England and Wales, where more than 20 million acres were classified as farmland.

Robert Bakewell, the well-known eighteenth-century agricultural innovator, is credited with being the first breeder to concentrate on the serious improvement of the heavy breeds of farm horse, giving preference to horses that could be traced back to the crossing of the large black horses from Holland with English horses in the late seventeenth century. Bakewell is said to have attached a great deal of importance to the constitution of his horses, in addition to aiming at a more compact body and cleaner legs – characteristics that are still considered of paramount importance by the breed societies today. The ideal farm horse that he succeeded in breeding, with its increased activity and tractable disposition, convinced all but a few diehards that the horse was a natural successor to the slower, less manageable ox in

11

A four-horse team ploughing in tandem. Museum of English Rural Life, Reading

an age when agriculture was increasing in importance and also undergoing great change in methods. Before the heavy agricultural horse was finally accepted, though (and before it had developed into the magnificent animal it is today), a number of sceptical farmers compromised by combining teams of oxen and horses, which were yoked together for ploughing purposes. More often than not, a pair of heavy horses replaced a team of four or six oxen; similarly, a team of four horses took the place of twelve oxen. An added bonus for the then progressive farmer who bought horses for cultivation and draft work was the fact that horses did not need a young boy or man to lead them, whereas teams of oxen did. This transitional period from oxen to horses did, however, mean that the farmer, or one of his employees, had to be well versed in horse management. Correct feeding, varying with the seasons, and the care of legs and feet were all important factors, essential to the welfare of the horses and to keeping them in peak working condition.

As the eighteenth century neared its close farmers and commercial carters fully appreciated the strength, stamina and commendable activity of the biggest breeds of horse, many insisting upon either Shires, Suffolks or Clydesdales for their individual enterprises. (The Percheron – not a native British horse – was not to be introduced in Britain for another 100 years or so.) In addition to extensive use in agriculture, horticulture and forestry (teams of heavy horses were employed to haul great tree trunks on long timber wagons from forestry areas to the saw mill), considerable numbers of heavy horses were employed by the railway companies. During the early 1920s over 19,000 horses were in use with railway companies throughout the

country for road delivery service and for shunting duties in yards. This figure fell to about 14,000 just before World War II, when fewer than 550,000 horses were employed even for work on the land. Twenty years later, the number of horses working on farms had dropped to a tenth of this figure. A number of commercial companies also kept large numbers of the heavy type of horse for road haulage and deliveries. Over 900 horses were stabled by four major London breweries, making daily deliveries of beer from the breweries to public houses in central London. At the beginning of the twentieth century one of the largest transport and removal firms employed over 2,000 horses for pulling their vans. Heavy horses were also used for hauling barges on canals, and for pulling coal delivery carts and millers' flour wagons, and several town councils kept between 80 and 100 horses for pulling refuse carts within the built-up areas under their jurisdiction. During the first quarter of the twentieth century, before the internal combustion engine began to be widely adopted for buses, delivery vans and heavy lorries, the use of heavy horses in commerce and agriculture reached its peak.

After World War II the almost total mechanization of agriculture and horticulture in Britain caused the number of heavy horses actually employed on British farms to decline with increasing rapidity. Thankfully the heavy horse has by no means been eliminated altogether, and even today, in the 1970s, there are still farmers, particularly those in the horticultural industry, who maintain that the horse is far more suitable than the tractor for their needs. They claim that horses are especially suitable for working on very wet land, and on heavy, uneven ground. Horses are still used for collecting

A photograph taken about 1910 of wagons on a Yorkshire farm.
Roy Shaw

13

mangolds and flowers, as they cause much less damage to the soil than heavy tractors. They are often used in the fen counties where sugar beet is extensively grown, and in other parts of East Anglia where the soil is light and sandy. Some foresters still prefer the more manoeuvrable horse – particularly for pulling out single tree trunks after felling has been carried out within a closely wooded area – to the weighty tractor. On the continent where, in certain districts, the development of farm mechanization and, in particular, the adoption of the tractor have not been as total as in this country, the use of farm horses has not decreased to the same extent.

The essential requirements of a heavy draft horse are the same today as they were over 200 years ago, and include great muscular strength; considerable stamina, enabling the horse to withstand long hours of continuous and sometimes arduous work in all weathers and in difficult conditions; and a docile, amenable temperament. In agriculture, working horses of this type should ideally weigh at least 17–19 cwt and stand between

Without the horse, its first successor on the farm – the traction engine – cannot operate. A subtle irony! Two horses in tandem hitched to a two-wheeled water cart are used to refill a traction engine's boiler. John Tarlton

A south midland type of spindle-sided bow wagon. Guy Villiers

Ploughing in seed potatoes on an Essex farm. John Tarlton

15

Ploughing with horses on a farm in Cumbria. Tom Parker

16 and 17 hands high. The outstanding characteristics of the four main breeds will be covered in greater detail in Chapters 2–5.

Depending upon the severity of the work undertaken and the standard of its upkeep over the years it is employed, the life of a heavy horse working on the land may extend well beyond 20 years – some have been known to exceed 30 years of age. As they mature between three and four years, it is not usually necessary to replace a team of farm horses more often than every 16–17 years – a period which has more often than not been exceeded. How often is a tractor replaced? And how efficient is it when approaching the 20-year mark? Horses, unlike machinery, do not start depreciating as soon as they are put to work; the reverse is true. Although well able to work long hours during the day, horses do require regular periods of rest, obviously at night if they have been working for long periods during daylight hours. This, in fairness to the tractor, is where it scores over the horse, as it can be driven well into the night when necessary. However, horses do not, barring unforeseen accidents, need extensive repairs or costly maintenance. Replacement parts for horses are confined to shoes, and very occasionally to harness. Admittedly there are times during the lifetime of a horse when a veterinary surgeon may have to be called in, but these occasions are hopefully rare providing that the horse is adequately fed in relation to the work it does, and that it is properly housed during the bleakest months of winter.

As opposed to regular payments for the delivery of fuel for tractors, the farmer using horses can provide oats, hay and straw for bedding from his own enterprise. Hay and corn – generally oats – form the basis of a working horse's rations, the daily quantity depending upon the size of the horse, the amount of work undertaken, and the time of year. An average ration could consist of 14–20 lbs oats and 15–20 lbs hay, plus some bran, except during the summer months when plenty of green fodder is normally available. Additional and alternative foods can be provided, depending upon their availability and on the season. These include maize, barley in the straw, carrots, dry beans, sliced roots, swedes, mangel wurzels, bran mash, oat straw and turnips.

An added dividend for the horse-owning farmer is that, if he keeps mares, from the age of three to four years they will produce foals. The gestation period is some 48–49 weeks, and the ideal time for foaling is during the months of April and May, when the young foal can benefit from the warm summer months on green pasture.

For the present preservation of the four breeds of heavy horse in this country, tributes must be paid to the dedication of the horse societies who represent the individual breeds; to the exacting breeders, so essential for the continuance of heavy horses; to the small band of enthusiastic farmers who steadfastly refuse to yield to total mechanization; to the devotees of the horse ploughing associations; and to the large brewers who not only display their horse-drawn carts at horse and agricultural shows, but who, in some instances, continue to use horses for transporting beer in busy, built-up areas not too far from their breweries.

It is my sincere wish that this book will help to bring back nostalgic memories of a less frenzied past to the older reader, and at the same time, if only in a small way, create a resurgence of interest in all four breeds of heavy horse that have served us so well and continue to give so much pleasure wherever they are seen.

2.
The Shire

Three alert young Shires. Miles Bros

The Shire has long been considered by many eminent authorities in the equestrian world to be the best heavy horse ever bred in Britain. As mentioned in Chapter 1, it is claimed to be the purest surviving descendant of the early type of medieval Great Horse or English Black Horse. The Shire's size and strength owe a great deal to the heavy continental breeds imported into Britain between the fourteenth and seventeenth centuries. Shire horses evolved in several of the midland shires, as well as in the fenland areas. The earliest stallions – in the sixteenth and seventeenth centuries – are said to have come from Leicestershire, Derbyshire and Staffordshire. Towards the end of this period and in the eighteenth century, Shires were also being bred by farmers in Lincolnshire and parts of the midlands, including Oxfordshire. The ultimate development of the Shire during this period, certainly by the eighteenth century, resulted in one of the largest horses in the world, indisputably the biggest British horse, and one that was quite comparable with the heavy breeds of Holland and Belgium. One contemporary chronicler wrote that the largest Shire horses in the whole country came from the county of Leicestershire, where they were used not only for pulling heavily laden wagons and drays, but on occasions were also employed as coaching horses because of their exceptional strength and powers of endurance. Later on, Shires were crossed with the blood horse, or thoroughbred, to produce a faster, less massive type of coach horse.

The earliest type of Shire horse had a great abundance of rather coarse hair, sometimes on the knees of the forelegs and on the rear of the hocks, as well as the hair that grew in profusion on the fetlocks, neck and tail. Hair was also to be found on the upper lip. Perhaps unfairly, it was said that most of these over-hirsute examples of the Shire originated in Lincolnshire. If one has the temerity to suggest that this overabundance of coarse hair was partly bred out by crossing the east coast and midland Shires with Clydesdales, or the Clydesdale-type horses of Cumberland and Northumberland, then the benefit can be considered a mutual one – one John Paterson of Lochlyoch, for instance, is said to have imported a black English stallion to cross with his Clydesdale mares, thereby increasing the bone and general size of the native breed. Shire stallions have also been crossed with hunters for a number of years to improve the bone of hunters – a necessary development to contend with the heavier members of society who have taken to the hunting field!

One of the earliest records of a stud Shire stallion is that of a horse known, curiously, as the Packington Blind Horse, which lived between 1755 and 1770 in the village of Packington, near Ashby-de-la-Zouch, Leicestershire. Another notable pedigree Shire from the same county was *Blaze*, foaled in 1770, whose descendants fetched up to 500 guineas even in those days. References were also made in this period to the black stallions of Derbyshire, which may well have descended from the dark-coloured horses imported from Holland in the sixteenth and seventeenth centuries. It was the aim, even in those early days, to establish and then maintain a uniformity of type, appearance and character, and to keep accurate records of accredited brood mares and stud stallions conforming to a set standard.

Whether employed for work on the land, or for haulage on the roads and elsewhere, the essential qualities demanded of the Shire include great strength, a strong constitution, exceptional stamina, docility of character, adaptability, and a relatively light and active movement. Physically, stallion

Field Marshal V, *bred and owned by King George V, champion at the Shire Horse Society's 1920 show at the age of three years.* Museum of English Rural Life, Reading

Freedom from the restrictions of harness and dray for four of Whitbread's Shires. Whitbread & Co. Ltd

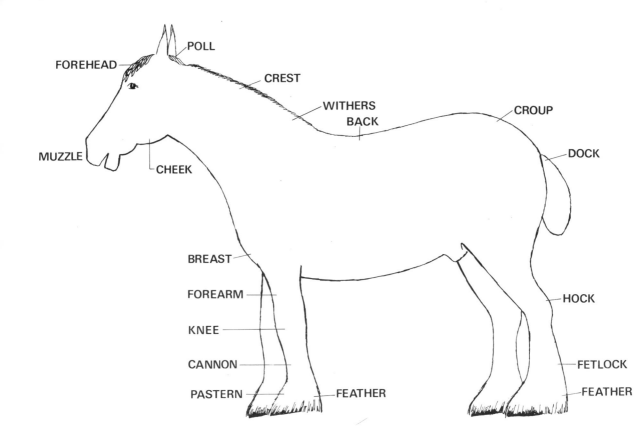

POINTS OF THE HORSE

Shires should ideally stand between 17 and 17.2 hands in height, and mares a little smaller at 16–16.2 hands – representing heights of 5 ft 4 ins at one end of the scale to a little over 5 ft 8 ins at the other, measured from the ground to the withers. Girths vary from 5 to 8 ft, depending on whether the horse is a stallion or a mare. Normally, fully-grown stallions of 17 hands weigh between 18 and 22 cwt, and mares, due to their slightly smaller stature, are proportionately less heavy, generally between 17 and 19 cwt. Additional physical characteristics should also include a lean head with long, sharp, sensitive ears and fairly large, prominent eyes; a broad forehead between the eyes; long, slightly arched neck; short, strong, muscular and gently curved back; wide, powerful quarters; well-proportioned legs, which in more recent years have seen a reduction in the amount of fine, straight, silky hair (feathers); and deep, solid feet, a little wider for the mares. In colour, Shires may be black, bay or grey. The present Shire Horse Society, known as the English Cart Horse Society for the first four years of its existence, was formed in 1878 to improve and promote the continuance of the breed and to keep authentic records of both sires and dams. In this way

Noble, *a seven-year-old dark bay gelding owned by the Hull Brewery Co. Ltd.* The Field

breeders were able to purchase or exchange stallions with a known history and thereby maintain a pure strain of heavy horse, now fully recognized throughout the world as the British Shire horse, an ideal type of draft horse for both agricultural use and a wide variety of commercial dray work.

In addition to hauling heavy loads and pulling farm machinery in Britain and other countries, Shires have also been used for pulling brewers' drays (one London brewer has used horses for over 230 years), railway wagons and delivery vans, canal barges, coal carts and heavily laden timber wagons. The weight-moving capabilities of the Shire have been quite dramatically demonstrated on numerous occasions. At one show a pair of Shire geldings yoked in tandem, and demonstrating their strength on wet, slippery granite setts, moved off pulling $18\frac{1}{2}$ tons behind them – the shaft (front) horse actually moving the load before the trace (back) horse had got into his collar. The same pair of horses also pulled against a dynamometer at the Wembley Exhibition in 1924. The maximum reading of the instrument was exceeded, and the pull exerted was calculated to be equal to a starting load of 50 tons!

As mentioned in Chapter 1, all four breeds of heavy horse can be seen at various shows throughout Britain, and the Shire Horse Society hold their annual National Shire Horse Show at the East of England Showground, Alwalton, Peterborough. The first of these now annual spring shows was held at the Royal Agricultural Hall in Islington, London, in 1880. There were twelve classes at this first show, five each for the stallions and mares, and two for geldings. In recent years, some of these shows have been held in association with the Percheron Horse Society of Great Britain, and stallions, mares and geldings, together with a variety of commercial turnouts have been seen in strong competition with each other. Other shows in which the Society takes an active interest include the Midlands Shire Foal Show and Sale – organized by the society of the same name – and the London Cart Horse Parade, which is held every Spring Bank Holiday in Regent's Park, London.

An idea of the value put on some of these magnificent animals can be gained from the following prices. At the Shire Horse Society's 1920 annual show, a Shire mare, *Gleadthorpe Seclusion*, was sold for the sum of 4,600 guineas, a figure that has not been exceeded to this day. The highest figure paid for a stallion is believed to be 4,100 guineas offered – and no doubt gladly accepted – for *Champion's Goalkeeper*, twice champion at the London show. These record prices were the exception rather than the rule, although during the early part of the twentieth century other superb Shires were sold for 2–3,000 guineas.

An impressive number of outstanding Shires – stallions and mares – are listed in the Society's stud books, published annually each March. Over 185,000 stallions and mares have been registered with the Society for the last 90 years. Recorded for posterity, challenging present-day and future generations of champions to surpass them – if they have the temerity to do so – are a considerable number of magnificent and often prolific sires with an impressive lineage. These include several stallions which rose to prominence in the late nineteenth century, among them one – *Honest Tom* by name – which was champion stallion at the Royal Show six years running (an achievement in itself), and which sired 139 registered Shires. In the same era, *What's Wanted* had 92 of his foals in the Society's stud books. *Harold*, a magnificent champion stallion of ten Shire Horse Society shows in the 1890s, was reared in Derbyshire and prospered for 20 years. The great majority of these early Shires could trace their origins to horses bred in Lincolnshire.

Mares also reached elevated pinnacles of perfection in quality, physique and character, and one of the greatest is said to have been *Erfyl Lady Grey*, five times a show champion, over 17 hands in height and weighing more than 22 cwt, with a 9 ft girth. (These figures compare with an average height for Shire mares of about 16 hands, a weight in the region of 17–19 cwt, and a girth between 5–7 ft according to age and size.) The sire of *Champion's Goalkeeper* also produced the champion mare, *Lorna Doone*, which carried off premier awards at the Society's shows during the early part of World War I.

In more recent years, *Ladbrook What's Wanted*, foaled in 1963, was champion stallion at the 1966 Shire show; *Layston Sunbeam*, born in the same year, became champion mare in both 1967 and 1968; and *Grange Wood William*, born in 1965, was a worthy champion at the 1967 and 1968 spring shows. One of the tallest Shires on record was claimed to be *Wandle*

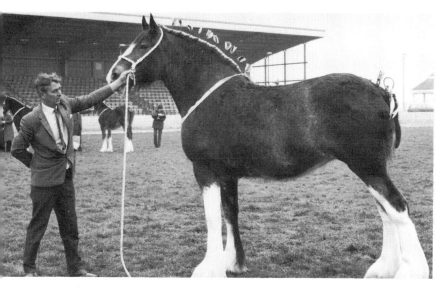

Wheelton Rose, a five-year-old bay Shire, supreme female champion at the 1974 National Shire Horse Show. The Field

Young's magnificent eight-horse team of black Shires effortlessly pulling a brewer's dray. Young & Co's Brewery Ltd

Robert, a gelding owned by Young and Co.'s Brewery Ltd, of Wandsworth, London. This truly magnificent horse was 18.3 hands (over 6 ft) tall, and in his prime weighed 1.04 tons.

At the Shire Horse Society's 1968 annual show, held at Peterborough on the East of England Showground, the total number of entries passed the 100 mark, and was the highest for over 15 years. To mark the occasion a marathon drive by five teams of heavy horses took place between the 22nd and 24th March. Starting at Peterborough, the teams were driven in relays, the last team being driven to Buckingham Palace where a letter was delivered to the Society's patron, Her Majesty the Queen, carrying greetings and informing Her Majesty of the Society's achievements in their 90th year. Each team of horses covered between 15 and 20 miles, and staging posts, as in earlier days, were arranged along the route so that horses could be changed and their drivers given appropriate and well-deserved sustenance for the journey. The final team reached Buckingham Palace just before 4 p.m. on Sunday, 24 March, thus completing a journey of over 80 miles.

A stallion premium scheme, similar to the one operated by the Hunter Improvement Society, was introduced by the Shire Horse Society in 1973, with the financial support of the Horserace Betting Levy Board. The main object of the scheme is to improve the type of stallion available for breeding and to encourage breeders to keep the right type of horse entire. The society hopes that this scheme will not only enable the owners of stallions to be more selective in the mares which are brought to the stallions at stud, but will also ensure the continued success of the society itself. A parade of premium stallions took place for the first time at the 1973 spring show, and a total of 33 premiums were awarded, amounting to £4,700. This figure included grants towards transportation of horses having to travel further than 100 miles from the Peterborough showground. In 1974 the stallion premiums were increased in value to a minimum of £150 for two-year-old stallions and £250 for stallions of three years and over. The 1974 National Shire Horse spring show saw the best turnout of horses for about 40 years. Entries were received from over 70 exhibitors from 24 counties and in all 116 horses were on show. The 14 classes included one-, two-, three- and four-year-old stallions; two-, three- and four-year-old geldings; fillies, mares; and teams of two, three or four horses in harness with vehicles.

Markets overseas have not been neglected by British breeders, and the first Shires were probably exported to America over 100 years ago, in the mid-nineteenth century. From this time on, breeders became more and more aware of the Shire's export potential. After the USA, which now has its own Shire Horse Society, the largest purchasers of Shires were Canada and South America, followed by Australia, Germany and Russia. Even today, in an age of almost universal mechanization, an average of 20 registered Shires are exported annually. Enquiries from the USA indicate an upward trend of renewed interest, where, it is reported, some farmers are reverting to horses following the oil shortage and the reduction of supplies from the Middle East. A special committee, appointed by the Shire Horse Society, inspects all horses before export from this country to ensure that these animals are suitable examples of the ideal type of English Shire.

With a resurgence of interest in horses generally, and in the breeds of heavy horse in particular following their decline soon after World War II due to mass mechanization, prices for Shire horses have risen steadily over the last few years. Amounts now being paid for Society-registered mares and stallions, whether required for showing, breeding or working purposes, have reached a peak. Today, between £500 and £1,000 is being paid for a three-to four-year-old Shire stallion; between £600 and £700 for a four-year-old gelding; and up to £1,500 for a really first-class brood mare with, or in, foal. Six-month-old filly foals cost between £500 and £600, and colts are sold for £200–300, but sometimes reach £500. Working horses, other than the large geldings required by the breweries, may be brought for £300–400. On this basis a farmer may purchase a working horse, new harness and a new cart for £600–700 – a figure considerably less than the amount required for a new tractor! It is estimated that approximately 1,200 Shires are at present employed for working on farms, for pulling brewers' drays, and similar duties. Equally encouraging to those of us who are concerned about the future of the heavy horse is the existence of about 100 breeders of Shire horses in Britain at the present time. If the average number of stallions, mares and foals owned by each Shire breeder is taken as 18, this raises the total number of Shires throughout Britain to about 3,000 – an increase of approximately 1,000 horses over the last ten years or so.

3.
The Suffolk

Suffolk mare and foal. Miles Bros

The Suffolk, sometimes known as the Suffolk Punch, is a native of East Anglia and takes its name from the eastern county situated midway between the Wash and the River Thames. The lineage of the breed can be traced back to the eighteenth century, when they were firmly established as a distinctive strain, and all Suffolks can trace their descent to a horse which was foaled in the village of Ufford in the year 1760. The main characteristics of the breed at that time varied very little from the salient points of the present-day Suffolk, over 200 years later. From the early introduction of other strains, including Norman stallions, with finer features, greater activity and a better-looking outline, the Suffolk has developed into a very beautiful horse, which has been described by one ardent admirer as 'one of the most beautiful of our domestic animals'. All non-essential, extraneous elements from those early days of improving the breed have now been eliminated, as has the earlier tendency to imperfect sidebones.

The chief characteristics of the ideal Suffolk are indomitable courage, a gentle nature, exceptional constitution, great endurance, intelligence, and a smooth, well-balanced, active movement. The horse has a long, active life, which has frequently reached nearly 30 years; an early maturity, enabling light work to be undertaken at the age of two; a docile disposition, which means young horses can be quickly schooled; freedom from grease and sidebone; and the ability to subsist and to work on a very limited supply of rations, when related to the size and work-capability of the horse. The latter quality may well be due to the practice in the past of infrequent feeding on the farms of East Anglia. The Suffolk became sufficiently adapted to these conditions to work for many hours without food in bulk, subsisting all day on a small allowance of corn and possibly some irregular grazing during the summer months.

In appearance, the Suffolk may be any one of seven shades of chesnut (invariably spelt with only the one 't'), ranging from almost brown-black through mahogany and a dull dark chesnut to a light, mealy chesnut. The most popular and the commonest colour is a bright reddish chesnut, which is referred to as a lively shade, a little lighter on the flanks and generally with a white star or 'blaze' on the broad forehead. The mane and tail are sometimes almost flaxen in colour. Physically, Suffolks have a deep, tapering neck which merges into long, muscular shoulders that are somewhat lower than those of the Shire, giving the Suffolk considerable pulling power. The deep, well-rounded body with impressive width both fore and aft, and the wide hips, have led to the breed sometimes being known as the Suffolk 'Punch'. The Oxford Dictionary offers this definition of the word 'punch': 'a short fat man, or anything short and thick'. Having said that, it is probably true to say that the Suffolk has a softer, more graceful appearance than the other three breeds of British heavy horse. This impression may well be influenced by the longer body, finer head and shorter, less heavy legs, which should be short and straight with sloping pasterns, and free from coarse hair. The feet should be hard, sound and medium-sized. The majority of Suffolks are 16–16.3 hands in height, and are almost as heavy as Shires, weighing between 17 and 20 cwt. A five-year-old champion Suffolk stallion is on record as having weighed as much as 23 cwt, with over 11 ins of bone below the knee. Another exceptionally large champion was a horse called *Monarch*, which measured 17.5 hands and had an 8 ft 4 ins girth.

A distinguished authority on heavy horses has described the Suffolk as

Champion Suffolk stallion Happy Valley Jason, *owned by Mr C. Saunders of Hoxne, Norfolk.* Monty

'the agricultural horse *par excellence*' – it was in fact bred principally as an agricultural draft horse particularly suitable for farms with heavy soil, which are typical of East Anglia. Before the advent of the tractor, the Suffolk was extensively used for ploughing, harrowing, drilling, harvesting, and for pulling heavy loads of sugar beet, mangolds, timber, corn and chalk. Its sound, medium-sized hooves make the breed very suitable for horticultural work.

In addition to these varied farming duties, Suffolks have in the past been used for drawing delivery vans, shunting railway trucks, and similar work in dock areas. They have also been used for pulling millers' flour wagons and coal delivery carts in London and elsewhere. Some years ago now, a well-known London firm of coal merchants used Suffolks for coal delivery. One of their horses, purchased when a three-year-old, worked for 17 years, during which time it conveyed many thousands of tons of heavy coal without ever having a day's illness – a fine testimonial, if one is needed, of the breed's exceptional constitution and powers of endurance. Suffolks were purchased by city corporations and district councils throughout Britain for pulling refuse carts, and were also used by the Great Eastern Railway company at Ipswich for delivery van services in that part of East Anglia. It has been claimed that the Suffolk has been employed for a wider variety of work than any other British heavy horse.

A fine pair of Suffolks belonging to Truman's, hitched to a brewer's dray. Truman Ltd

During World War I, pure-bred and cross-bred Suffolks were used by artillery battalions for hauling guns and for transporting military supplies on the battlefields of France and Belgium where, during the winter months, conditions were appalling for both man and beast. The Suffolk is also well able to withstand considerable heat, and for this reason it has been exported to hot countries such as South America and Australia. The breed adapts well to the hot climatic conditions of the sandy veldt of South Africa, particularly as their legs are free from excessive hair and most Suffolks have been bred on the light-soil areas of East Anglia.

Following the formation of the British Suffolk Horse Society in 1877, whose aims were to trace the history of the Suffolk horse and to establish essential characteristics for the future accredited stallions and brood mares, the first Suffolk stud book was produced. This valuable document took nearly three years to produce, under the painstaking editorship of Mr Herman Biddle of Playford, who was a founder member of the Society. By the early 1940s, membership of the Society had risen to about 2,000 members, and it is heartening to learn that new members are still being enrolled even today.

Suffolks have been shown extensively at a number of annual shows throughout the country, particularly at the Woodbridge Horse Show,

normally held every Easter Monday; the East of England Show; the Suffolk, Essex and Royal Norfolk Shows; and the Royal Show, at which in 1973 over 50 Suffolks were entered.

One of the outstanding Suffolk champions of more recent years – during the mid-1950s – was a wonderful stallion named *Springfield Commander*, which was foaled on a March, Cambridgeshire, farm in 1949. This remarkable stallion won no fewer than 24 championships, including five 1sts at the Royal Show, during only six years of showing. Another fine champion Suffolk stallion to reach his peak towards the end of the 1960s was *Happy Valley Jason*, foaled in 1965. Winner of 14 championships over a four-year period, including that of champion Suffolk stallion at the Royal Show as a four-year-old, he is owned by Mr C. C. Saunders of Oakley Park Stables, Hoxne, near Diss, Norfolk.

Some 30 or 40 years ago, more studs of pure-bred Suffolks had been established in the USA than in any other country, following the importation of top-class stallions and mares. The breed has been deservedly popular for a number of years, and an American Suffolk Horse Association is in existence which publishes its own Suffolk stud book, in which it is acknowledged that the breed is the 'ideal farm horse' providing the essential qualities of 'constitution and soundness'. Suffolks have achieved an equally high reputation in New Zealand, Canada, Germany and the USSR. A further affirmation of the breed's excellent constitution is the testimonial given some years ago by an Australian owner, Mr C. G. Tindall. He purchased his stallions at shows in Britain, and then employed teams of horses in his native Australia for draft purposes, often covering several hundreds of miles between one destination and the next, and for the most part only on rough tracks. Operating under these testing conditions, this particular owner stated that his Suffolks stood up to the heat well, were quite capable of living on the road, and often came off a journey in better condition than when they started out. He also successfully crossed his English stallions with the native mares in Australia.

An English farmer submitted an unsolicited testimonial to the British

An unusual job for a Suffolk – pulling a game-collecting cart during the shooting season. John Tarlton

Suffolk Horse Society, comparing pure-bred Suffolks with unspecified cross-bred agricultural horses. Two farms were worked, similar in size and with the same type of soil. On one, 24 cross-bred horses were employed, and on the other farm 25 Suffolks were used. The available feed was the same for both enterprises and included hay, mangolds, corn and chaff. The cross-bred horses required 75 lbs of corn each week, compared with 50 lbs for the Suffolks. This difference was even greater when comparisons were drawn between the Suffolks and the oldest of the cross-bred horses, which needed an extra 14–21 lbs of corn per week to maintain them in peak working condition. It was estimated that using pure-bred Suffolks in place of the cross-bred horses of similar stature would result in a saving of nearly 9 cwt of corn over a 40-week period – a not inconsequential saving, even in the heyday of the farm horse, and more so today when corn prices have soared to dizzy heights due to reputed world shortages. This farmer had further praise for the Suffolks he employed, adding that, unlike the cross-breds, the Suffolks had never suffered from either grease or sidebone – a bonus, though admittedly difficult to translate into economic terms.

As municipal draft horses far removed from the peace of the countryside, Suffolks were employed many years ago by the Glasgow Corporation Cleansing Department, and comparative costs at that time were calculated by the superintendent in charge. The object of the exercise was to compare the economics of horses with those relating to electrically driven vehicles. The city refuse was collected within an area between one and a quarter and one and three-quarter miles from the refuse destructor. It was found that, within these distances, horses were a much more economic proposition; savings increased in inverse proportion to the length of journey undertaken.

To sum up, the outstanding characteristics influencing the selection of Suffolks for agricultural work both in this country and overseas are a hardy constitution, early maturity, low food consumption, versatility and a long life. With regard to the longevity of the breed, one remarkable mare is on record as having foaled at the venerable age of 37, but this, it must be admitted, is an exception, as most foal-producing mares are in their early twenties.

33

4.
The Clydesdale

*Full dress will be worn – Colonel, a Clydesdale,
kitted out with basic harness and decorations.
(Note the ear caps; the housen attached to the
hames; the brow band with horse brass; the trace
chains; the martingale with brasses; the
embossed decorative blinkers; and the mane
decoration.)* Lee Weatherley

The Clydesdale is the Scottish equivalent of the English Shire, and derives its name from the area called Clydesdale in earlier times, and now known as Lanarkshire. One of the earliest breeders is believed to have been a Mr John Paterson of Lochlyoch, who, like the sixth Duke of Hamilton, introduced Flemish stallions into the Clyde valley area between 1715 and 1720, to improve the size and weight of the native breed of draft horse. Other chroniclers of this period state that the stallions and mares of Lochlyoch were inter-bred with the English Shire, which was a larger horse than the local breed, at that time a much smaller horse than the one known today as the Clydesdale. One of the earliest Clydesdales on record is *Glancer*, foaled some time after 1810, by a mare descended from the Lochlyoch strain.

The emergence of the Clydesdale as a distinctive breed of heavy horse was greatly influenced by several stud-registered stallions in the mid-nineteenth century, which were all sired by the same stallion, a descendant of a stallion from Aberdeenshire, which had been crossed with a mare from the Clyde valley area. At that time landowners, farmers of lesser means and coal merchants were all actively involved in breeding the Clydesdale. Motivated by the need for a larger farm and draft horse, Clydesdales from Lanarkshire were inter-bred with the local horses of Wigtown, Kirkcudbright and South Ayrshire in the mid-nineteenth century, and were known as Galloway Clydesdales. Certain areas of Aberdeenshire, Argyllshire and other parts of Ayrshire are also said to have influenced the development of the breed in this period. Further inter-breeding took place with the horses from Cumberland and Westmorland, which were mostly grey in colour and had very similar characteristics to the Clydesdales from over the border.

Compared with the English Shire, which on occasions it closely resembles, the Clydesdale is slightly less massive (not so broad-chested, or so deep in the body), is smaller-boned, with longer, well-proportioned legs, and in temperament is, in some cases, less placid than the Shire. The Clydesdale has a straighter, less heavy face, with an open forehead, broad between the eyes, wide muzzle (less Roman in profile), large nostrils and ears, and nearly always a white face between the eyes. The neck is long and well arched (crested) to a short back; the breed has sloping shoulders, a well-sprung, barrel-like rib cage, broad, muscular quarters and high withers. The all-important feet should be round and open, with long pasterns, set at an angle. Particular stress is given to the quality and soundness of feet and legs. Another characteristic of paramount importance is a perfect combination of weight, size, strength and activity. Many breeders consider the ideal colour to be dark brown, but many Clydesdales are bay in colour, and occasionally grey and black are seen. In addition to the white face, almost all have white legs below the knee. More often than not they have more hair, with feathers on the fetlocks, than the Shire of today – a feature which did not increase their popularity in the USA, where a clean-limbed horse is now preferred. Although the average hight is about 16.2 hands, a number of stallions and geldings are as tall as 17 hands, and weigh about 18 cwt. At all times the ideal Clydesdale should give the impression of a good-looking, active and powerful horse with an amenable temperament.

Although employed initially for ploughing and other farm work, the Clydesdale was extensively used by commercial concerns for hauling timber and transporting coal from the Scottish coalfields, as well as for coal delivery in urban areas. Other users included city corporations, which generally

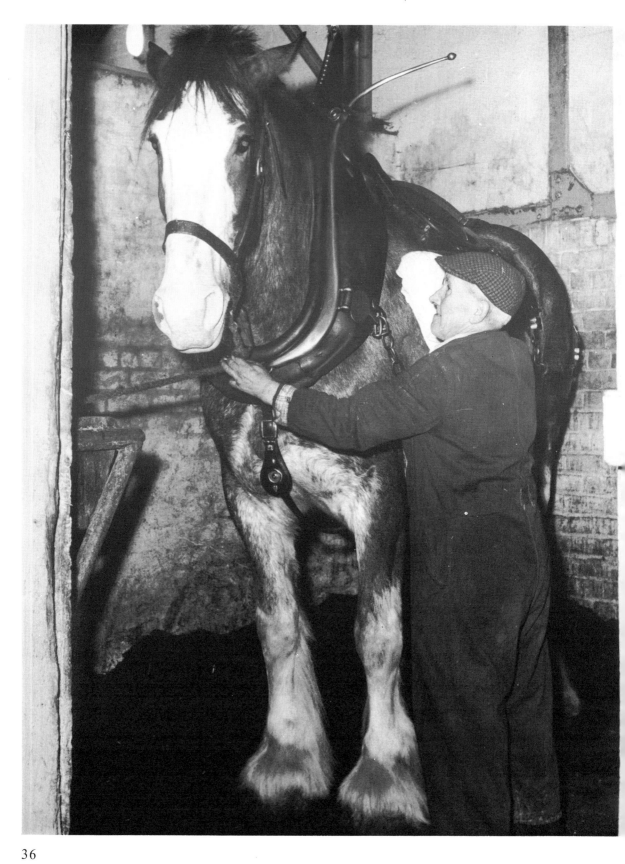

employed the horses for up to 12 years or so, after which they were
purchased by farmers for less arduous duties on the land.

A splendid family of Clydesdales in
the lowlands of Scotland.
Tom Parker

The Clydesdale Horse Society was formed in 1877, and a year later it
published its first stud book which contained over 1,000 registered stallions.
Over 80 volumes of the stud book have now been produced, and the total
number of stallions has risen to more than 25,000, with about three times
this number of mares. Following the early introduction of Flemish stallions
and horses from the northern counties of England to produce a heavier,
larger-boned draft horse, the society made every endeavour to maintain a
distinctive Scottish breed, which would be universally recognized as the
Clydesdale, and which would not be predominantly influenced by other
breeds outside Scotland, in particular those from England.

In addition to farmers in the midlands, southern England, Wales and
Ireland adopting the breed, a great number of Clydesdales have been exported
during the last 130 years to Canada, the USA, New Zealand and Australia.
In Australia they were used for hauling large quantities of wool from the
sheep-shearing sheds. Like the Shire and the Suffolk, the Scottish horse has
also been exported to several European countries, including Germany and
the USSR. At the height of their popularity, when heavy draft horses were
considered an essential part of agricultural life, as many as 1,000 Clydesdales
were exported in a 12-month period. Both New Zealand and Australia
imported the breed as far back as 1850, in fact before the foundation of the
Clydesdale Horse Society. The American Clydesdale Horse Association was
formed in 1879, two years after the British society, but active promotion and

A working Clydesdale owned by
Buchanan's getting a rub-down after
a day's hard work in the city of
Glasgow. James Buchanan &
Co. Ltd

breeding in the USA are no longer of any real significance.

Over the years, Clydesdales have been shown at a number of major horse and agricultural shows both in Scotland and elsewhere. During the early part of the nineteenth century, the Highland and Agricultural Society, formed towards the end of the eighteenth century, inaugurated a system of premiums to promote certain breeds of Scottish horse, and awards were allocated to separate classes of Clydesdales. Later in the nineteenth century, the Glasgow Agricultural Society promoted an annual stallion show at which the finest specimens of the breed were exhibited, enabling breeders to maintain a high standard of breeding stallion at their studs. Clydesdales often collected premier awards at these shows – one such horse was *Prince of Albion*, who won first prize for four consecutive years (1887-90) at the Highland and Agricultural Society shows, and was later sold as a two-year-old for the sum of £3,500. An even higher figure – £4,260 – was paid for *Benefactor* when he was sold at Netherhall in 1925. *Dunure Footprint* was another outstanding stallion, reigning as champion sire from 1915–27. *Ambassador*, foaled in

Winston *and* Jim, *a fine pair of Clydesdales owned by Mr R. H. Corbett, with ploughman Jim Sheffield in charge.* Lee Weatherley

1937, was bought for £5,880. However, even he was surpassed by *Baron of Buchlyvie,* who held sway at the beginning of this century and after carrying off premier awards at the Highland and Agricultural Society show was sold at auction at Ayr for the record sum of £9,500.

Splendid examples of Clydesdales at their best are still being shown today at many Scottish shows, including those at Glasgow, Ayr, Lanark and Kilmarnock. At the Royal Highland Show in 1973 the premier award for a stallion went to Mr Peter M. Sharp's *Bardrill Enterprise,* after the same two-year-old had been awarded the championship at the Scottish Stallion Show, held in Glasgow earlier that year. For many years, a popular event at the American International Show was the parade of teams of horses, and in particular those of the heavy breeds. Between the late 1950s and the early 1960s ten premier awards were won by a six-horse team of Clydesdales belonging to Wilson and Co. Inc. of Chicago – a far cry indeed from the origin of the breed over 200 years earlier in far-off Lanarkshire, nearly 4,000 miles away.

5.
The Percheron

Regal Lady *and* Lady Ideal, *prize-winning Percheron
mares, earning their keep on one of Chivers's farms
before the advent of mechanization.* Chivers
Farms Ltd

The Percheron, although not a native British heavy horse, is extensively employed by farmers and others in the British Isles. It takes its name from the Le Perche district of France. This is an area of about 60 square miles, to the south-west of Paris, where farmers have been breeding this very distinctive type of draft horse since the early nineteenth century with considerable success.

According to old chroniclers, the Percheron is one of the most ancient French breeds, and is said to have origins as far back as 782, following the defeat of the Saracen chief Abderame by Charles Martel at the battle of Poitiers. The Saracens' fine Arabian cavalry horses were requisitioned by the victors, and were later dispersed throughout France, particularly in the Le Perche district. Later still Rotrou, the Earl of Le Perche, who had been on a crusade abroad, imported several oriental stallions which were crossed with local mares. It is therefore assumed that the Percheron has definite Arabian origins and over the years, due to further crossing with horses from Western Europe, and possibly Turkish strains, it has developed into the considerably larger breed it is today. Just as the English Suffolk horses can trace their descent in the male line in an unbroken chain to a horse foaled in 1760, the modern Percherons can trace their ancestry to one of the greatest stud stallions of the breed, *Jean-le-Blanc*, foaled in 1823 at Orne, which fully exhibited all the features cherished by Percheron breeders over the years.

During the nineteenth century, Percherons were used in France as agricultural horses and for pulling mail – and stagecoaches. It is said that a wealthy American, travelling in France in 1815, was so impressed with the Percherons harnessed to the coaches in which he travelled that he bought them on the spot and took them back with him to America! The Percheron in France reached the height of its popularity between 1880 and 1920, when thousands of them were exported to North and South America, Australia, South Africa, Japan, Italy, Spain and Russia.

The Le Perche area of France is located on the borders of Maine and Beauce in Normandy, extending into the districts of Orne, Sarthe, Loir and Cher, and officially restricted to 50 sub-districts. The land has a high limestone content, and is mostly apple orchard country. Other parts are cultivated by arable farmers, with some land under plough and some kept as pasture land, mostly well watered by numerous streams. It is claimed that this environment has contributed to the particularly strong bone structure of the French Percheron.

The breeders of the Le Perche area prefer horses that are grey in colour, mainly because they resemble the original Arabs, but also for the more practical reason that grey horses are easier to find in the middle of a dark night than animals of a darker colour! Other characteristics considered essential by French breeders include an even temperament, attractive appearance, considerable strength and size, relatively short legs, and a general all-round toughness. In general build, Percherons are not normally so large as Shires, but are heavier than Clydesdales with more bone and muscle. British Percheron stallions should not be less than 16.3 hands in height, and mares at least 16.1 hands when fully grown, weighing 18–20 cwt and 16–18 cwt respectively. French-bred horses are a little heavier than those produced in Britain. A number of foals are born almost black; many remain this colour, but the majority develop into grey or dapple-grey adults, generally with a minimum of white. Both skin and coat should be of a fine quality. The limbs

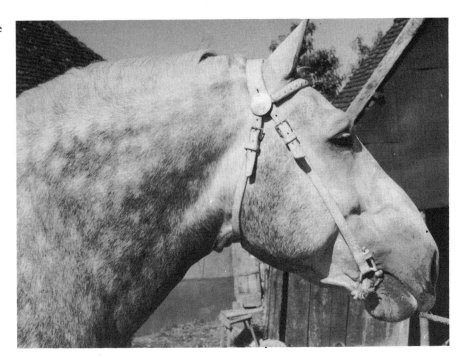

A French Percheron. Soc. Hippique
Percheronne de France

A Percheron mare. Miles Bros

and feet of the Percheron have admirably withstood the exacting demands of the past, which at one period included working on the stone block roads of France as well as the cobbled streets of London, where the breed was for many years used for pulling omnibuses.

Percherons are willing workers, fully capable of pulling heavy loads for continuous periods without undue strain. A pair will take up to $2\frac{1}{2}$ tons nett load (almost 4 tons gross) on the old type of dray, and even more when the vehicle is equipped with rubber-tyred wheels. Due to the breed's strength, admirable constitution and almost complete lack of nervous tension, a pair of Percherons are well able to average daily journeys up to five miles each way and with loads up to $2\frac{1}{2}$ tons, in busy, built-up districts, without any adverse effects.

In France, brood mares are distributed to selected farmers on whose farms they are put to work to ensure that they do not lapse from the peak of condition and that they maintain their physical toughness and their willingness to work. This makes certain that future foals can be said to come from a genuine working strain of horse – one that is actively employed for draft purposes. New foals stay with their mothers for a period of six months. Then a few months later those that have been selected for eventual breeding or sale are transferred to a breeder who has the responsibility of gradually building them up to maturity, ideally in the valley of the Huisne, where the grazing land is said to be unsurpassed. The breeding of Percherons in France today is now completely influenced by economic considerations. Although the demand for a working horse is now greatly reduced compared with the past, breeding these horses is still a profitable business. Prices of Percherons compare favourably with other breeds of French heavy horse. As in most other western countries, the mechanization of agriculture in France has reduced the number of horses used on the land, but there are farmers who have retained Percherons for draft work, supplementing tractors. Ploughing is probably the principal activity for which these horses are employed on French farms today.

On a rather unfortunate note, a number of Percherons are sold for their meat – which could, perhaps, account for the heavier build of the French horses – and when purchased for this purpose, as much as £500 is paid nowadays for adults in good condition. It is deeply regrettable to horse-lovers that each year France imports about 150,000 horses to meet the needs of butchers, and that there is a considerable market for animals for human consumption.

Of the approximate total of 300,000 heavy horses in France in 1974, between 50,000 and 60,000 were Percherons, either pure-bred, cross-bred, or of Percheron descent, and in the main they are located in the centre or west of the country. Each year, about 700 Percherons are registered in the French Percheron Society (*Société Hippique Percheronne de France*) stud book. This number, although encouraging at the present time, compares with 5–6,000 some 50 or 60 years ago. Export of these horses is no longer considered important – a few are still exported to South Africa, South America and China, and each year the Japanese visit France to purchase Percheron stallions. It would seem that diminished demand together with the high cost of transportation has greatly reduced the number of animals sent to the USA. The French Percheron Society organizes an annual breed horse show, usually in one of three regions (the Orne, Sarthe and Mayenne), which

A team of Percheron mares at a ploughing match. Guy Villiers

attracts a large number of devotees from France and other countries. At Le Mans in 1973 nearly 200 Percherons entered for the various classes. Members of the British Percheron Society who attended this event reported that the French horses were very uniform in type and gave the impression of greater size than their British counterparts. Prices were on the high side and the initial asking price for the fillies was often over £1,000.

The importation of the breed into Britain during World War I led to the formation of the British Percheron Society in 1918, and during the following four or five years 36 stallions and 321 mares were brought to Britain. By the mid-1940s, the total number of pure-bred Percherons registered in Britain had risen to over 3,000. Membership of the society correspondingly increased until it numbered nearly 500. Following the inauguration of the Percheron Norman Horse Association of the USA in 1876, the Percheron Horse Society of America was formed in 1905, and by the late 1960s over 250,000 Percherons had been registered. As well as the Percheron Horse Society of America, there is a very active and thriving Percheron association in Canada, with its headquarters in Alberta. Interest in the Percheron breed in Canada is now at a higher level than it has been over the last 40 or so years. A number of new owners have purchased mares for breeding purposes; others buy Percherons for draft duties on farms and forestry plantations; and some have bought them for showing with wagons and carts. The majority of the

Pinchbeck Union Crest, *champion Percheron stallion, bred and owned by Mr G. E. Sneath.* Lee Weatherley

association-registered horses are black, and this colour is more in favour in Canada than the greys or other colours. Canadian-bred Percherons give the impression of having slightly more rotund, heavier hindquarters, but, surprisingly, are more slender in the leg than those horses imported from France. A British-bred yearling filly, *Limelight Lady,* is already making her presence known in the show ring, collecting second prize in her class at the 1973 Royal Agricultural Winter Fair held in Toronto, Ontario. *Limelight Lady* was sired by that compact, fine-standing stallion, *Histon Limelight,* foaled in 1962 and owned by E. Bailey and Sons of Willingham. Cambridgeshire, England.

Following importation of French Percherons into the USA, where demand steadily increased from the middle of the nineteenth century up to 1916, the first pure-bred Percherons were then imported into Britain. During World War I many hundreds of both pure-bred and cross-bred Percherons were purchased from Canada, the USA and the Argentine (countries where the breed had become very popular as a draft horse) for military purposes. The British Expeditionary Force used them to haul heavy, unwieldy guns through the thick Flanders mud, and on roads which had become too rutted for mechanized transport; military supplies were transported in similar conditions; stabling was often very primitive, sometimes non-existent; and rations, on occasions, below the accepted minimum. The way the Percheron

45

A Jaffa orange publicity cart drawn by two Percherons owned by Mr C. Boyde. Citrus Marketing Board of Israel

withstood these appalling conditions confirmed for many the breed's ability to tolerate extreme hardship. This factor and several more admirable characteristics influenced British breeders and farmers to employ Percherons for agricultural work after the war was over.

The Percheron is claimed to be one of the most good-natured and tractable of all breeds, without being in any way sluggish. This trait of docility and unflappability was a particularly valuable asset when Percherons were handled by inexperienced horsemen and when they were moved from the natural environment of the farm to that of a busy, noisy town. At one time, before the invention of petrol- and diesel-engined buses, the breed was used for drawing London omnibuses. This would not have been possible had their temperament been at all suspect.

Despite the almost complete dominance of machinery in agriculture, Percherons can still be found on farms in some parts of Norfolk, Cambridgeshire, Lincolnshire and Durham, and elsewhere in smaller numbers. Like the Suffolk and the Shire, Percherons have been crossed with thoroughbreds, producing excellent heavyweight and middleweight hunters, exhibiting both strength and considerable stamina, and well capable of withstanding the demands of a day's hunting.

As with the other breed societies, one of the main aims of the British Percheron Society is to encourage the breeding of a pure strain – essentially one with clean, relatively short legs; a short back; ample bone; powerful, and

A Percheron confidently stepping out on the first circuit of the show ring. Monty

Pinchbeck Union Crest, *five times champion Percheron stallion, and champion stallion at the 1974 British Percheron Society show at Cottenham.* Lee Weatherley

47

at the same time active; eager to work; and with a good tractable temperament. Ideal features for the pure-bred Percheron as stated by the society include widely-set, full, docile eyes; erect, medium-sized ears; strong, not too short neck, fully arched in the case of stallions; wide chest, with deep, well-laid shoulders; strong, short back; wide and deep ribs; hindquarters of exceptional width; relatively short, strong legs, free from excessive hair; and feet of a reasonable size with good-quality hard blue horn. Only stallions that are either grey or black can be accepted for entry in the British Percheron Society stud book. Brown, chestnut and bay-coloured Percherons are therefore not so popular with the purists.

Chivers Farms Ltd, the well-known firm of fruit growers and conserve manufacturers, at one time owned several thousand acres of fruit farms, mostly in East Anglia. They employed on their various farms 150 horses, the majority being pure-bred Percherons, and the rest cross-bred horses with more Percheron than any other breed in their blood. Although the company are now completely mechanized, one of the last Percheron stallions bred by Chivers Farms Ltd, and now owned by the Cambridgeshire breeders E. Bailey and Sons, is that fine horse *Histon Limelight,* born in 1962, junior champion at the Royal Show as a two-year-old, and subsequently supreme champion at the same show. One of the greatest living authorities on British Percherons, and former chairman of Chivers Farms Ltd, is Mr J. Stanley Chivers of Impington, Cambridgeshire, who still maintains an active interest in the British Percheron Society.

Percherons can be seen at a number of British shows including the Royal Show, the East of England and Royal Norfolk Shows, and at most ploughing society events. After a lapse of some years, the British Percheron Society are once again promoting their own shows, which in 1974 was held at Cottenham racecourse, and included classes for stallions, mares, foals, fillies, geldings and turnouts. In addition to the Racehorse Betting Levy Board approving grants for stallion premiums amounting to £500, the society have been fortunate in obtaining sponsorship totalling £500 from J. R. Parkington and Co. Ltd, the London wine importers. Another nine firms contributed a further £397 between them, prior to the 1974 show, as a practical indication of their interest and support of the Percheron breed.

Every now and then one of the four main breeds of heavy horse produces a physically outstanding horse. One of the heaviest horses in Britain in the early 1970s was a champion Percheron stallion, *Saltmarsh Silver Crest,* owned by one of the leading British authorities on Percherons, Mr G. E. Sneath of Pinchbeck, Lincolnshire. Foaled in 1955, this magnificent stallion was 18.1 hands in height – about the same as *Wandle Robert,* an equally impressive Shire, owned by Young and Co.'s Brewery Ltd – but weighed a little more at 1.23 tons, with a girth of 8 ft 4 ins. *Saltmarsh Silver Crest* was deservedly one of the most impressive attractions at a Horse of the Year Show parade, and is now enjoying a well-earned retirement. With over 50 years of experience as one of Britain's top breeders, Mr Sneath believes that one of his finest mares is *Pinchbeck Lola,* sired by *Saltmarsh Silver Crest.* Although now owned by one of the major breweries, this favourite mare has produced a wonderful 18.2 hands black stallion, *Pinchbeck Union Crest,* who was supreme champion at the 1973 Royal Show. This superb stallion weighs between 22 and 23 cwt, and has an even greater girth than his famous grandfather!

6.
Heavy Horse
Harness and Decorations

Lucy, *a 12-year-old Shire, between the shafts of a
Kell seed broadcaster at the 1974 Lambourn
ploughing match. (Note the fly-terret between the
ears; the cart saddle with bells; the face piece;
and the martingale with five traditional brasses.)*
Guy Villiers

Correctly fitting harness is essential for the efficient performance and health of a working horse. The type of harness used depends on the nature of the work to be undertaken, which may vary from relatively light agricultural work on the land to pulling a brewer's dray on the roads.

One of the most important items of equipment is the collar, generally of the neck type. It should fit comfortably on the shoulders, at the base of the neck, and should never rub or chafe the animal, or restrict its breathing in any way. The basic shape and padding of a neck-type collar is always designed to fit the horse well but comfortably, and to give freedom both at the base of the neck and at the throat.

The main padded body of the collar incorporates a frame, made either of metal, or part metal, part wood, to which chains can be attached. The open prongs, or to be more correct the hames of the collar, which project upwards in front of the withers, are secured by means of a top latch. On either side of the collar are metal mountings, or hame hooks, to which the trace chains are fastened.

A rectangular or sometimes circular section is often seen, located behind the upper part of the collar and fastened to the hames. This is known as a housen, and in bad weather it protects the upper part of the horse and harness.

Breast collars, as their name suggests, encompass the chest instead of the neck, and are really more of a band than a collar in the true sense of the word. They are only used for light duties which do not in any way tax the horse's strength, and are used when a horse is harnessed to a light, two-wheeled carriage for one or two passengers.

A bridle or head harness is necessary for the horseman to keep effective control over the movements of the horse at all times. In addition to the bit in the horse's mouth, to which the reins are attached by means of a ring on either side of the mouth, the bridle has a pair of vertical straps, one down each side of the face. Two horizontal bands are attached between these straps – one below the ears across the forehead, and the other across the nose above the mouth. Yet another strap comes down from the top of the main vertical side strap at each side, to encircle the cheek.

Heavy horses, whether ploughing or pulling a brewer's dray, almost invariably wear blinkers. These are stiff leather flaps secured to the bridle to prevent the horse from being distracted or frightened by a sudden, unexpected movement. Most blinkers are decorated with a small patterned horse brass.

A saddle is not essential, except when the horse is placed between the two shafts of a wagon or cart, when a cart saddle is needed. This type of saddle is built up on a wooden frame known as a tree. The size and shape of tree used depend on the general physique of the horse. Padding is fastened to the sloping wooden sections, with or without some form of covering; there is a bridge across the apex; and straps are positioned along the ridge, fore and aft, for attaching to the collar and crupper strap. Additional straps are provided for fastening to the girth band. Provision is also made for connection with the breechings, which are placed over the back and hindquarters and generally consist of vertical and horizontal leather straps attached and suspended from the crupper strap which lies along the back behind the saddle. Breechings enable the horse to have control over the unwieldy bulk of the cart, particularly when undertaking other than straightforward manoeuvres.

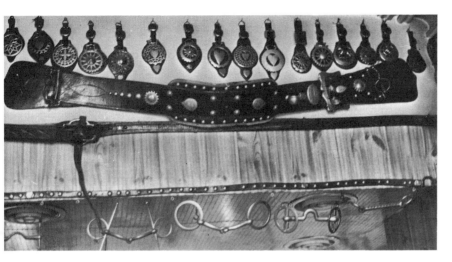

Horse brasses and other decorations – part of the collection of horse harness at the Croft Inn, Hythe, Hampshire. Guy Villiers

A three-horse team hitched to iron whipple- or swingle-trees. Museum of English Rural Life, Reading

Chains can be attached to the bridge of the saddle, suspended vertically to take part of the weight of the cart shafts and to keep them at the correct angle. Different parts of the country have, over the years, produced distinctive types of saddle with variations on the basic parts.

Saddles are not necessary when the horse is used for ploughing and other agricultural work. Trace harness, attached to the collar, is used instead. Attachment to a body band ensures that the chains are kept away from the horse's legs, and this type of harness is used when two or more horses are used in tandem, for ploughing, harrowing or drilling. The traces – chains or leather side-straps – are attached to the collar hames and held up well above ground level by straps suspended from the crupper, or fastenings on a half or full body band across the horse's back.

The trace chains from the collar are finally fixed to a whipple-tree – a

A grand pair of Shires. (Note the fly-terrets attached to the head strap; the plaited manes; the housen attached to the hames; the horse brasses on the martingale; and the hame hooks on the hames, accommodating the trace chains.)
Miles Bros

horizontal iron or wooden bar suspended behind the horse. The whipple-tree has two chain hooks, the distance between them being greater than the maximum width of the horse to ensure that the traces do not rub against the horse's side while it is working. When two, three, or even four horses are working in tandem, there is only one spacing bar or tree, located behind the last horse in the line. When horses are yoked two or three abreast, each horse has its own tree, with a third or fourth tree behind the individual trees. There are many variations in the way in which two, three, or more horses may be yoked abreast, involving several different types of tree.

Before concluding this section on harness, it should be mentioned that over the years a very wide variety of different types of saddle, collar, bridle and other forms of harness have been developed, each type indigenous to a particular part of the country, and dependent on the amount of progress made in farming implements and techniques.

The attractive, almost musical jingle of brightly gleaming horse brasses and chains is synonymous with the appearance of heavy horses at agricultural shows and ploughing matches. When at work on the farm, the amount of brasswork is generally kept to a minimum, with perhaps a single brass

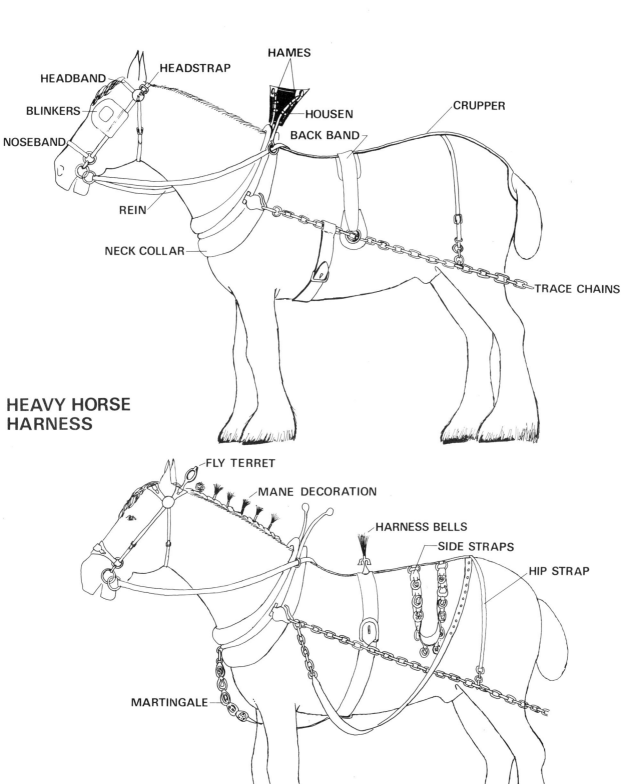

HEADBAND
HEADSTRAP
HAMES
BLINKERS
HOUSEN
NOSEBAND
CRUPPER
BACK BAND
REIN
NECK COLLAR
TRACE CHAINS

**HEAVY HORSE
HARNESS**

FLY TERRET
MANE DECORATION
HARNESS BELLS
SIDE STRAPS
HIP STRAP
MARTINGALE

**HEAVY HORSE
DECORATION**

decoration between the eyes, or fastened to the blinkers or cart saddle.

Horse brasses as such date back to the eighteenth century and are thought to be a legacy of the days when charms were worn to ward off the 'evil eye' of disease and general ill-fortune. In other words, the horse brass began as a good luck talisman. Later, the brass charms were replaced by brasses bearing crests, mascots, trade insignia, etc. Breweries, carters, railway companies and even councils had their own special designs. Many different types have been produced over the years, varying from the simple crescent pattern to most intricate designs incorporating the Prince of Wales' feathers, St Andrew's cross of Scotland, the Irish harp, lions, horses, swans and many other subjects. The vast majority were contained within a ring which facilitated their manufacture. It has been estimated that over 1,600 different designs of both pattern and figure brasses are still in existence. These decorative brasses, mostly flat, were mounted and hung on leather straps, and on special occasions festooned over the horse's body. Up to four or five were often seen on the martingale, which, as far as the heavy horse is concerned, is the strap lying between the front legs of the horse, attached to the collar at one end and to the girth at the other. Horse brasses were originally hand-made, and then cast or stamped out in greater numbers as their popularity increased. A number of foundries in the midlands allocated a fair proportion of their output to the production of horse brasses.

Apart from the familiar horse brasses, many other types of brass decoration can be seen on animals taking part in ploughing matches and shows. These ornaments include bells, which may be mounted on the hames of the collar or on the saddle; decorated face pieces and hame plates; ear bosses and studs; and terrets, which often incorporate bells and are fixed to the head strap behind the ears. The bells – sometimes colloquially known as flyers – can be single or multiple fitments, often miniatures of the face pieces, frequently with plumes. They are probably a legacy of the days when ringing bells warned other road users of the approach of horses. The plumed type of flyer may be single, double, or three-tiered, and can be located on the cart as well as being worn as a head piece. Some flyers are made of multi-coloured hair mounted on the metal frame of the terret, with or without suspended bells. Two types of bell can be used – either the open, clapper type or the spherical version – mounted singly, or suspended in a group from a special framework.

The decoration of heavy horses on occasions extended beyond brass adornments and includes coloured wool and flower arrangements. Brightly-coloured ribbons were also incorporated when the horses' manes and tails were plaited. Indeed, a small band of dedicated horsemen from both farms and commercial enterprises, skilled in the craft of horse decoration, vied with each other for the premier awards at the various shows.

Ear caps – basically a functional item – are still worn by horses at ploughing matches. Their purpose is to obviate the irritation caused by flies buzzing relentlessly round a horse's head, and thus to reduce the almost constant shaking of the head.

One of the finest collections of harness and horse decorations can be seen for the price of a pint of ale at the Croft Inn at Hythe in Hampshire, and anyone interested in horse harness, agricultural implements, and many other aspects of rural life in the past should visit the fascinating Museum of English Rural Life at Reading University.

54

7.
Societies
and Associations

Mr E. Coward's bay Shire gelding, winner of the
single heavy horse with vehicle class at the
National Shire Horse Show, 1974. The Field

A number of associations have made invaluable contributions to the promotion, improvement and preservation of the main breeds of British heavy horse, and none more so than the four breed societies who still continue to foster the interests of those who breed, own and admire Shires, Suffolks, Clydesdales or Percherons. Their addresses, and the addresses of all the other societies and associations mentioned, will be found at the end of the chapter. Three of the breed societies have been in existence for nearly a century, and all four have one aim in common – to maintain the continued existence of a distinctive breed of heavy horse, conforming to the clearly defined standards specified by each society. Stud books are published by each breed society, enabling the antecedents of registered horses to be traced back over a number of years. The societies also organize their own shows, provide prizes and add to the stallion premiums awarded by the Horserace Betting Levy Board.

The Heavy Horse Preservation Society was inaugurated in 1973, following a donation of £300 from a Miss Lois G. Arthur of Chester, after a Mr Barber, past president of the British Federation of Master Saddlers (now the Society of Master Saddlers) had suggested the desirability of such an association. The society's main aims are to promote the use of heavy and commercial horses; to find new uses for heavy horses in a changing environment; to facilitate the supply of vehicles and harness, either for sale outright, or on loan; to assist and support existing users of heavy horses; and to offer accommodation for heavy horses that may become temporarily redundant. Soon after the formation of this society, a £10,000 fund was launched to enable them to accept responsibility for unwanted heavy horses, on the basis of an average cost of about £500 per horse. The society is based at Whitchurch in Shropshire, where they have offices, a large stable block and grazing land. Very largely a voluntary organization, the society welcomes contributions, however small, or donations of unwanted articles.

Another important group whose enthusiastic and dedicated members are actively concerned with heavy horses are the horse ploughing associations. Some of the major ploughing matches now have attendance figures of more than 2,000, and more and more matches are being arranged, with a greater number of teams taking part. This admirable band of very knowledgeable countrymen (and townspeople, too) fulfil three roles: they help to maintain an interest in all types of working heavy horse; they foster the ancient skill of the sadly diminishing number of horse ploughmen; and they keep alive a traditional rural way of life that is almost unknown to the younger members of our community who have, in the main, been brought up in an exclusively mechanical world.

One of the more active and consequently more successful societies in this category is the Southern Counties Heavy Horse Association. Formed in 1970 by a small group of enthusiasts in Surrey, membership from all parts of Britain passed the 500 mark within three years. The association's aims are to promote and encourage the art of horse ploughing; to promote horse ploughing matches; to encourage more people to compete in horse ploughing events; to foster interest in the heavy horse and its work, and to encourage young people to understand and possibly work with heavy horses; and to co-operate with other societies having similar interests. The association has adopted a recognized set of rules based on those governing the British National Ploughing Match. Turnout classes are also encouraged, as well as

classes for the best mare, the best gelding, and the best pair of horses. Membership is open to anyone interested in heavy horses and their activities.

Heavy horse societies are by no means limited to Britain. As an indication of the initial impact that the Shire made on the agricultural community of the USA and as a sincere compliment to the English breeders, the American Shire Horse Breeders' Association was formed in 1885, and as recently as 1967 an organization called the Maryland Shire Horse Associates was established. Unfortunately, in recent years, coinciding with a fall in demand, the senior American association has lapsed a little in its active promotion of the breed, but with Mr Orlin Waring as president and the appointment of a new publicity director there are now signs of a welcome resurgence of interest within the association. Contributory factors may well be the 1973–4 reduction in supplies of Middle East oil, the increased price of the oil that is available, and the fact that the present-day Shire is a much cleaner-limbed horse than its predecessors. Between 50 and 60 members are vigorously involved in importing Shires from Britain, and assisting and encouraging breeders in the USA to expand their studs.

*Champion ploughman 81-year-old
Jack Pearce working his team for the
'Golden Guinea' Trophy at the
S.C.H.H.A. meeting at Windsor,
1972.* J. R. Parkington & Co. Ltd

The Maryland association was formed by Mr Norbert L. Behrendt and
Mr Howard F. Streaker, both owning farms in that state. They aim to
preserve and promote the Shire breed, and to investigate its possible future
in the state of Maryland. Following the importation of English Shires, the
number of Shires stabled in Maryland has increased to 25, in seven years.
The organization is not only prepared to meet the demands of breeders and
others in the USA, but welcomes enquiries from other countries.

The American Clydesdale Horse Association was formed in 1879, two
years after the equivalent society for Great Britain and Ireland.

Percherons were first exported to America from France almost 160 years
ago, and were not seen in Britain until this century. The Percheron Horse
Association of America (formerly the Percheron Norman Horse Association,
and subsequently the Percheron Society of America) is therefore very much
the senior society outside France, the country of origin.

In 1910, there were over 5,300 Percheron breeders in the USA, and
between 1900 and 1910 the number of registered horses increased from
nearly 1,500 to over 31,800. During this period, a record price of $40,000
was paid for a Percheron stallion called *Carnot.* In the mid-1930s, about
100 American breeders decided that the ideal American Percheron should
be medium-sized, heavy-boned, 'up-headed', with stallions weighing 16–18
cwt (mares $13\frac{1}{2}$–$14\frac{1}{4}$ cwt), and standing 16–17 and 15–16 hands tall
respectively. The colour should ideally be predominantly grey or black, but
bays and sorrels would not be excluded from registration. Additonal
characteristics to be favoured by American breeders included exceptionally
well-muscled lower thighs; clean action; good quality feet and legs; a fairly
long croup with large, well-rounded hindquarters; close-coupled; and a wide
deep chest, with plenty of back rib. One of the most impressive Percherons
known to the American society is an American-bred horse named

Dr Le Gear, a dapple brown gelding, standing 21 hands high and weighing more than 26 cwt.

Percherons have always been very popular in Canada, and a considerable number were imported from France, particularly between 1880 and the early 1920s. The Canadian Percheron Association was formed in 1907 and has been located almost continuously within the province of Alberta. Each province has its own branch, and a director of the parent association is responsible for each of six geographical areas. The association is actively dedicated to the expansion of the Percheron in Canada: it formulates future policy; establishes registration and transfer fees; distributes literature; supervises breed activities; nominates breed judges; and publishes an annual breed review. Up to the end of 1973, a total of 20,212 Percheron stallions had been recorded in the Canadian stud book, which also contained a total of 25,647 mares at that date. The number of registrations issued each year is at present on the increase, and corresponds with the general expansion of the heavy horse industry in Canada, which has showed signs of a positive revival since 1970, after being in a state of depression for the previous 30 years. All registrations are maintained by a government-operated agency known as the Canadian National Livestock Records Agency, based in Ottawa. This agency issues registrations and transfers of ownership for the Canadian Percheron Association, as it does for all pedigree breed organizations in Canada. All membership fees, registration fees, transfer fees, etc. that are collected by the records agency are passed to the Canadian Percheron Association.

Compared with the American Percheron, the Canadian type should ideally be a larger, heavier animal which is active and has a certain amount of distinctive drive and character. Most of the registrations in the Canadian stud book are black in colour, but greys are almost as popular except when employed for promotional and show purposes.

No mention of the Percheron in any country can be made without at least a passing reference to the French association, the *Société Hippique Percheronne de France,* which was founded in 1883 by breeders in the Le Perche region. One of the aims of the society is to keep a very careful record of all authentic Percherons in the stud book, and no new animal is ever included unless both its sire and dam are already entered. This stipulation has applied since 1890. All foals in the stud book must be registered in the year of their birth, and up to the time of registration they may not be transported from their place of birth. Newly-registered foals must be branded by a qualified veterinary surgeon under the mane with an insignia representing the letters 'SP' intertwined – a legacy of the noblemen of Le Perche. The society organizes a number of shows which are held annually in one of the principal towns in the Le Perche area, such as Nogent-le-Rotrou, Mortagne, Laigle, Alençon, Ferte-Bernard or Mamers. The only horses allowed to take part at these shows are those entered in the society stud book. In this way, buyers can be assured that any horse bought will be one of genuine pedigree, already entered in the stud book.

A number of commercially orientated heavy horse societies have been in existence for many years now. The London Cart Horse Parade Society, for instance, was founded in 1885 with His Grace the Duke of Cambridge as patron, Baroness Burdett-Coutts as president, and Sir Walter Gilbey, Bart, as chairman. The society's objectives were to improve the general

A pair of Young's black Shire geldings, winners of their class at the 1974 National Shire Horse Show. The Field

condition and treatment of London's cart horses; to encourage drivers to take a humane interest in the animals in their care; and to encourage the use of powerful cart horses for heavy work on the streets of London. Much emphasis was also laid on the general care and cleanliness of these horses. The first London Cart Horse Parade was held in 1886 and attracted 150 entries. Following presentation of numerous prizes, the full entry of horses and vehicles paraded around Regent's Park, down Albany Street, Portland Place, Oxford Street, Tottenham Court Road and Euston Road to King's Cross. The following year the parade was extended to include cart horses stabled within seven miles of Charing Cross, which increased the entry to 383. Up to the outbreak of war in 1914 the entries actually had to be limited to 1,000, but increasing use of motorized vehicles caused a gradual decline

of numbers over the years, until in 1965 the entry totalled only 26.

At the suggestion of Lord Woolavington, the first London Van Horse Parade was held in 1904 and a society formed with similar aims to the London Cart Horse Parade Society. The parade has been held every Easter Monday for the past 70 years, except during wartime. The largest parade was in 1914 when a record entry of 1,259 horses was exhibited. After World War II the parade was again held with an entry of 204 in the first year, which increased to 365 by 1950; after this numbers gradually declined until 1962, when the size of the entry began to increase again. In 1963 227 vehicles were exhibited.

Following a meeting of the committees of both societies, it was agreed that from 1966 these two parades should be amalgamated under the title of the

London Harness Horse Parade, and that the annual show should be held on Easter Monday in Battersea Park. The parade is not a competition between the various entries: a standard is set by the judges and each exhibit attaining this standard receives a first class award. The essential requirements are that the horses must be well groomed, the harness must be well cared for, and the vehicle must be clean and in a good state of repair. The 1974 show was the 78th parade at which heavy horses were exhibited, and in the heavy horse classes 15 single-horse turnouts were entered, followed by seven pairs and three four-horse teams of heavy horses. Shires predominated in these classes with 32 entries, compared with six Percherons, a pair of Suffolks and one unspecified heavy cross-bred. Among the regular show exhibitors were five major brewery companies, Mr Carl Boyde, MRCVS, W. A. Lidstone Ltd, Mr R. P. Dash and Mr P. J. H. Workman. Headed by HM the Queen, over 100 individuals and organizations give generously to the annual prize fund of the London Harness Horse Parade Society.

Although, strictly speaking, neither a society nor an association, the bi-monthly publication *The Heavy Horse Magazine* plays an important part in publicizing and co-ordinating the various activities of all the breed societies, without any bias to one particular breed. Another welcome aspect of this publication is the amount of coverage given to forthcoming shows at which heavy horses will compete, followed by well-illustrated reports on these and other events. Mr R. J. Lomas, the dedicated and enthusiastic editor, deserves every encouragement and no small degree of praise for achieving the virtual amalgamation of the main breed societies in one publication, and for launching such a magazine when many pessimists are saying that the heavy horse has had its day.

Addresses in Great Britain

The Shire Horse Society, East of England Showground, Peterborough, Northants
The Suffolk Horse Society, 6 Church Street, Woodbridge, Suffolk
The Clydesdale Society, 24 Beresford Terrace, Ayr, Scotland
The British Percheron Society, Owen Webb House, Gresham Road, Cambridge
The Southern Counties Heavy Horse Association, Robertsley, Rowly Drive, Cranleigh, Surrey
The Heavy Horse Preservation Society,   Whitchurch, Shropshire

Addresses in the USA, Canada and France

The American Shire Horse Breeders' Association, Box 19, Pingree, Idaho 83262, USA
Maryland Shire Horse Associates Inc, 13720 Clarksville Pike, Highland, Maryland 20777, USA
The American Clydesdale Horse Association, c/o Mr Charles W. Willhoit, Batavia, Iowa 52533, USA
The Percheron Horse Association of America, c/o Mr Dale Gossett, Belmont Ohio 43718, USA
The Canadian Percheron Association, PO Box 9, Cremona, Alberta, Canada
Société Hippique Percheronne de France, 28400 Nogent-le-Rotrou, 7 Rue Villette-Gate (Eure-et-Loir), France

8.
Shows and Events

Daisy *and* Prince *belying their combined ages of 47
years at a ploughing match.* Guy Villiers

Horse shows, gymkhanas, agricultural and country shows and even horse ploughing matches have never been as popular with the general public as they are today, in the mid-1970s. Fortunately for the heavy horse enthusiast, interest in this type of horse has also increased over the last 5–6 years, and very few shows today do not include classes for heavy horses or for heavy horse turnouts.

The breed societies either organize their own shows annually, or give considerable support and encouragement to other shows at which individual breeds are invited to enter a variety of classes for both horses and turnouts. As an encouraging indication of the revival of interest in Percherons in Britain, the British Percheron Society held their own horse show, the first for Percherons only for 17 years, at Cottenham racecourse, Cambridgeshire, on 25 May 1974. About 3,000 people attended this show, which the society are now hoping will be an annual event. Entries were received for 48 horses in the 13 classes, which included stallions, mares, foals, fillies, geldings and two- and single-horse turnouts.

At this particular show, the veteran breeder and past president of the society, Mr G. E. Sneath of Pinchbeck, Lincolnshire, collected three firsts in the stallion classes and awards in the special classes. His *Pinchbeck Union Crest*, five times champion Percheron stallion, and senior stud sire at Pinchbeck, won Class 3 for stallions and the society's perpetual challenge cup for the best stallion in the show. This magnificent example of all that is best in the breed was then a ten-year-old, standing a little over 18 hands in height and weighing more than 22 cwt. Mr Sneath's son, Mr H. Edward Sneath, left the Cottenham show with two firsts, both gained by his grey gelding *Jolly*, foaled in 1968 and bred by himself. Three members of the Sneath family have been elected president of the British Percheron Society, and on one unique occasion Mr Sneath junior presented a champion challenge cup to Mr Sneath senior, who was president from 1960–1 and from 1972–3.

Several other distinguished breeders and Percheron owners exhibited at this show, including Messrs E. Bailey and Sons, who run a stud at Hempsall Farm, Willingham,Cambridgeshire, and own *Histon Limelight*. This animal, foaled in 1962 and bred by Chivers Farms Ltd, was supreme champion at the Royal Show and champion stallion at the 1962 Peterborough show. *Willingham Veronica* (born 1974), sired by *Histon Limelight* out of *Willingham Ruth*, won first prize for E. Bailey and Sons in the class for pure-bred or supplementary register foals at the 1974 Cottenham show. The Willingham stud, who export Percherons to Canada and Australia, also own a four-times champion mare of the breed, *Overcote Princess*, foaled in 1966. Another well-known exhibitor was Mr Carl Boyde, MRCVS, a Chertsey, Surrey, veterinary surgeon who was a founder member of the Southern Counties Horse Ploughing Association (now the Southern Counties Heavy Horse Association). Mr Boyde has done a great deal in recent years to ensure that many heavy horses destined to be put down enjoy several more years of well-earned retirement. At Hardwick Court Farm, Chertsey, he keeps horses which may be hired, together with appropriate vehicles, for exhibiting at shows or for publicity purposes. The company who market Jaffa oranges regularly hire Percherons – more often than not *Cabaret* and *Flower*, who have also performed with some distinction at horse ploughing matches – from Mr Boyde's stables.

A number of Percherons recently imported from France were entered at Cottenham, and one, *Cabine,* a six-year-old grey mare owned by Mr T. W. J. Mott of Little Downham, Ely, won Class 4 and the challenge cup for the best pure-bred mare in the show. Mr Mott obviously recognizes an outstanding mare when he sees one, as his *Fen Anna* had earlier been judged supreme champion at the Royal Show. In the turnouts, Mr J. E. Young from Corringham, Essex, won both the single- and the two-horse classes, with Mr C. Boyde runner-up in both classes. Mr J. E. Young also won the silver challenge cup presented by Chivers Farms Ltd for the best two-horse turnout. A rather unusual entry in the turnout classes was an early twentieth-century fire engine harnessed to two willing Percherons! Awards were made

Royal Show — before the judging — a brewer's dray drawn by a pair of Shire black geldings. John Tarlton

Grooming a Young's Shire before taking part in the annual Greater London Council Horse Show on Clapham Common. After thorough washing, the white feathers are being dried with fine sawdust.
Daily Telegraph

to stallions of three years and over, which were considered to be of sufficient merit to obtain a premium under the scheme which has been made possible by a grant from the Horserace Betting Levy Board of £500, with an additional £100 donated by the British Percheron Society. Financial sponsorship and various donations received by the society totalled more than £900, in addition to a number of very fine challenge cups presented by individuals and companies.

Heavy horse enthusiasts from all over the country attended the 1974 National Shire Horse Show held at the East of England Showground, Peterborough. Under the auspices of the Shire Horse Society, the show had the best entry for about 40 years, and included stallions, mares, geldings and various turnouts. Entries were received from over 70 exhibitors from 24 counties, and in all 116 horses were on show. The 14 classes included one-, two-, three- and four-year-old stallions; two-, three- and four-year-old geldings; mares, four years old and over; one-, two- and three-year-old fillies; and teams of two, three or four horses in harness with vehicles. One of the main features of the show was the award of stallion premiums which that year were increased in value to a minimum of £150 for two-year-old stallions, and £250 for stallions of three years of age and over. This no doubt influenced the initial entry of 49 eligible stallions in the three appropriate classes. In all, a total of 38 premiums were awarded by the judges. An extremely high standard was achieved in all classes and *Woodhouse Footprint*, a three-year-old stallion owned by Mr L. Fountain from Marston Montgomery, Derbyshire, became the 1974 supreme champion, collecting the King George V champion challenge cup. The supreme gelding champion was a three-year-old bay, *Cowerslane David*, owned by Mr T. Yates of Windley, Derbyshire; and *Wheelton Rose*, a five-year-old bay, owned by L. Joseph and Sons, won the class for four-year-old mares and was judged supreme female champion.

Several Shire owners entered four or more horses in the various classes, including E. Coward Ltd of Thorney, who later in the year entered a pure-bred registered mare and a filly at the British Percheron Society show at Cottenham; and Mr J. R. Suckley, owner of the Alneland Shire stud at Oswestry, Shropshire, whose *Elian Grey King*, sired by *Alneland Masterpiece II* (champion stallion at the 1971 Royal Show) won the yearling colt class. *Quixhill Masterpiece*, owned by Mr J. Salt of the Quixhill Shire stud at Denstone, Uttoxeter, won the class for two-year-old colts against 14 other entries. Mr Salt took another first prize back to Staffordshire when his five-year-old bay, *Quixhill Gay Lad*, let for the season to the Great Eccleston Society, won the class for stallions of four years and upwards. Both these fine stallions were sired by *Quixhill What's Wanted*, and their dam was *Burnham Beauty* by *Minoan*. At the Royal Lancashire Agricultural Society show at Ribby Hall a few months later, *Quixhill Masterpiece* won first prize in the stallion – yearling – two-year-old class for Shires, and *Quixhill Gay Lad* won the three-year-old and over stallion class, and in addition was reserve to the Parkington 'Golden Guinea' Shire Horse of the Year qualifier, *Tremoelgoch Princess Anna*, owned by Mr G. Lloyd Owen. At this same major show in the north-west, Mr R. Hull from Stanley Farms, St Michaels-on-Wyre, collected a first and three seconds in the Shire classes. *Cowerslane David*, supreme gelding champion at the National Shire Horse Show, gained two firsts in the gelding classes, including champion gelding of any age, for his owner, Mr T. Yates from Windley, Derbyshire.

Returning to the National Shire Horse Show at Peterborough, the breweries were, as usual, well represented in the harness classes for heavy horses in harness with a vehicle. However, in the single heavy horse turnout class it was the Northamptonshire farmers E. Coward Ltd of Thorney, Peterborough, who triumphed over excellent entries from five well-known breweries and five other exhibitors. Their entry, four-year-old *St Vincent's King William*, had had only five months' experience in harness with a vehicle. A fine pair of black geldings owned by Young and Co.'s Brewery Ltd, London, won the pairs in harness class, and in the class for a team of three or four horses Watney Mann Ltd returned to their Whitechapel brewery with a first prize gained by their team of bay geldings.

Later in 1974, the Peterborough showground was the venue for an annual show of major importance – the East of England Show – which attracted an attendance of more than 114,000 over the three days it was on. Heavy horses were by no means forgotten among the other livestock classes, and there were several classes for Shires, Suffolks and Percherons. Champion Shire of the show was Mr H. Eady Robinson's filly, *Lillingstone Again*. Following his success at the National Shire Horse Show earlier in the year, Mr T. Yates

Cross-bred Clydesdales Lucky *and* Linda, *hitched to a nine-tine, two-horse cultivator.* Guy Villiers

gain did well with his *Sleightwood Miss Fashion* (best brood mare); *Cowerslane Trueman* (best foal); and *Cowerslane Gem* (best yearling). Many of the prize-winning Percherons at the Cottenham show were again well to he fore. *Willingham Veronica* repeated her first in the foal class for E. Bailey and Sons, whose *Overcoat Princess* was judged champion Percheron. E. Coward Ltd were again awarded first prize for their single heavy horse urnout, and Young and Co.'s black geldings repeated their earlier success on he same showground by winning the pairs in harness class. Shires also won he team of three or four horses in harness class, Courage's fine bays collecting the premier award.

Although a relatively new show, the Royal Show, now held annually at the National Agricultural Centre at Stoneleigh, Warwickshire, is generally accepted as the premier agricultural event of the year. Many of the country's most impressive heavy horses are exhibited in the various classes for Shires, Suffolks and Percherons, which are judged individually and in the heavy harness events. In the 1974 Shire classes, Mr J. Salt's two-year-old bay, *Quixhill Masterpiece*, won his class and went on to be judged champion Shire stallion of the show. *St Vincent's King William*, the four-year-old bay owned

A ploughman's less glamorous view of proceedings during a horse ploughing match. Guy Villiers by E. Coward Ltd, carried off the senior gelding prize after winning the Shire gelding class at the Suffolk County Show a few days previously. The overall Shire champion and best female was *Lillingstone Again,* the filly owned by Mr H. Eady Robinson. Champion Suffolk stallion *Happy Valley Jason,* winner at the Suffolk County Show, was also judged champion Suffolk stallion at Stoneleigh. Owned by William C. Saunders, this grand ten-year-old stallion had previously carried off the premier award at the Suffolk Show on five occasions. Having won firsts at both the Royal Norfolk and Suffolk County Shows, *Laurel Countess,* owned by P. Adams and Sons Ltd, gained the champion female award at Stoneleigh. Not surprisingly, Mr G. E. Sneath's Percheron champion stallion, *Pinchbeck Union Crest,* was judged overall Percheron champion and best stallion. Champion female in the Percheron class was H. Garner and Sons' *Tinkerbell,* which was also awarded a first at the Royal Norfolk Show.

In the heavy harness classes at the Stoneleigh show, Courage's bays again won the Shire team first prize, with E. Coward Ltd winner of the single-horse turnout. William C. Saunders won the Suffolk team class, and Essex farmers Mr and Mrs Clark won the Suffolk single-harness class. Vaux Breweries won both the team and pairs in the Percheron classes, and Mr H. E. Sneath gained first prize in the Percheron single-horse turnout event. William C. Saunders also collected two firsts in turnout classes at the Suffolk Show, where Mr and Mrs Clark again won the single Suffolk turnout; E. Coward again won the single-Shire horse turnout; Young and Co.'s Brewery the Shire pairs; and Watney Mann the Shire team class. All these successful exhibitors who vie with each other at the various shows up and down the country again did well at the Royal Norfolk Show, where the Solid Fuel Advisory Service's *Limington Viking* won first prize in the Shire gelding class, later won the single heavy harness class, and was judged champion of the turnout classes.

Although the Royal Windsor Horse Show, held over four days in the Home Park, Windsor, caters more for hunters, showjumpers and ponies, classes are included for light and heavy trade and agricultural turnouts. In the 1974 heavy single-horse turnouts, Young and Co.'s Shire gelding won first prize, and Courage's Shires won both the pairs and the prize for the champion team. At the 1974 Shropshire and West Midland Show, held at Shrewsbury, Mr T. Yates' supreme gelding champion of the 1974 Shire Horse Society Show, *Cowerslane David,* was again judged the best two- to three-year-old gelding and 'Golden Guinea' champion. It was a thoroughly successful show for Mr T. Yates, as he also returned to Derbyshire with three more firsts and a third place in other Shire classes, including a repeat success with *Sleightwood Miss Fashion,* again judged best brood mare of the show. Mr J. R. Suckley's yearling colt *Elian Grey King* collected another first, and the prize for the senior gelding class want to *Grove Captain,* owned by W. A. Lidstone Ltd from Taplow, Berkshire.

Sponsors and donors play a very important part at shows that include heavy horse classes. They not only enable the organizers of these shows to arrange appropriate classes for individual horses and turnouts, but provide an added incentive to breeders and owners of heavy horses to exhibit. J. R. Parkington and Co. Ltd, shippers of French and German wines, are one of the major sponsors of heavy horse events throughout the country. The company have inaugurated the Parkington 'Golden Guinea' Shire Horse of

the Year championship award, awarded at the Horse of the Year Show at Wembley. Qualifying rounds are held at the following shows, held between May and August every year: the Shropshire and West Midlands Agricultural Society Show at Shrewsbury; the Royal Show at Stoneleigh; the Great Yorkshire Show at Harrogate; the East of England Show at Peterborough; and the Royal Lancashire Show at Wrea Green, Preston. In addition to a splendid bronze model of a Shire horse mounted on an onyx plinth, the total prize money awarded at the Horse of the Year Show amounts to £180. Parkington also pay out a transport grant for those horses travelling to Wembley for the final.

The company's first active participation in the heavy horse world was at the World Ploughing Championships which were held at Taunton in 1971. On this occasion, support was given to the horse-drawn classes, for which no fewer than 21 pairs were entered. Since that date, Parkington have extended their support to ploughing matches throughout the country. One such event was the Southern Counties Heavy Horse Association's ploughing match held in Windsor Great Park in 1972, when 28 pairs assembled before some 15,000 spectators – confirmation of the very keen interest that such events now arouse. Parkington are very enthusiastic about the considerable revival of interest in the heavy breeds of horse, and hope that their sponsorship will in some way contribute to the survival of these magnificent animals.

Sponsorship of a financial nature is also given to the National Horse Ploughing Match and the Cructon and District Horse Ploughing Match for the British Isles Championship. At the time of writing, support is also given to the Suffolk Horse Society at three shows – the Woodbridge Horse Show, the Suffolk County Show, and the Framlingham Show; and to the Percheron Society at the Cottenham Show. Contributions are also made to farm and trade turnout classes at seven shows. Southern British Road Services have arranged with the Shire Horse Society to sponsor classes for the breed at four shows in their region. In addition, Southern British Road Services make donation to the Shire Horse Society to assist with general administrative costs at these shows. This new sponsorship applies to the Suffolk County Show, the South of England Show, the Essex County Show, and the Kent County Show. Regional sponsorship is also given by Bass South-West, who presented the Worthington E trophy to Mrs Rosemary Elliot for the best horse shown in hand at the 1974 West Coker show.

Every spring and summer there are a number of horse and agricultural shows, horse sales and other country events at which classes are specially included for heavy horses and heavy horse harness turnouts. There are too many to mention them all by name, but in addition to those already referred to, the following shows are well worth a visit: Soham, Cambridgeshire, where a heavy horse show is held each year; Newbury, Berkshire; Oswestry; Lincoln; Bakewell; and Gorefield, near Wisbech. Judging at these and other shows is normally based on conformation to type as recommended by the appropriate breed society; physical condition and soundness of the horse; and action – movement of the horse, both at the walk and at the trot. The show organizers of the 1970s are well aware of the general public's real interest in the heavy type of horse and heavy horse turnouts, and whenever possible include special classes for Shires, Suffolks, Clydesdales and Percherons, accompanied by championship cups, trophies, money prizes, and premiums for the stallion classes.

9.
The Role
of the Breweries

Two fine Shires, Bob *and* Baron, *in the shafts of a
delivery cart owned by* Wadworth & Co. Ltd,
*of Devizes, Wiltshire, and used for beer
delivery.* Wadworth & Co. Ltd

As already mentioned in other chapters, a number of breweries not only take a pride in parading their splendid heavy horses and drays at agricultural shows and ploughing matches, but still continue to use these horses for transporting beer in built-up areas. Apart from agriculture, brewing is the only industry still actively employing heavy horses for draft work. Admittedly, one or two breweries just keep their magnificent horses for prestige purposes, and these continue to be a major attraction wherever they are paraded. A considerable debt is owed to all those breweries who retain stables of horses, whether for work or show, or both.

Whitbread and Co. Ltd, the well-known London brewers, have used horses since the formation of the company in 1742. They probably keep more Shires than any other commercial organization at the present time. The firm's 16 horses, which are normally bought from breeders for up to £600 as four-year-old geldings, pull the brewers' delivery drays for between five and six hours a day. During the summer months, the horses are given a well-earned rest at the company's hop farm at Beltring in Kent. They are retired when they are 15–20 years old. Traditionally, each year, six of Whitbread's dapple-grey Shires are given the privilege of pulling the Lord Mayor's ceremonial coach through the streets of London in the Lord Mayor's Show.

Two other equally well-known London breweries who have extensively employed Shire horses for a number of years are Young and Co. Ltd of Wandsworth, and Watney Mann Ltd. In 1885, new stables were erected for Mann, Crossman and Paulin (as the company was originally known) in Cambridge Heath Road in the east end of London, to accommodate the 150 Shires which were used at that time for all beer deliveries to public houses in the central London area. It is sad to recall that in 1941 the stables were hit by a land mine, which killed 25 horses and injured at least another 70. By the end of World War II about 100 horses were regularly employed by the brewery. These Shire horses once again began to take part in shows in the early 1950s, but the previous policy of showing only greys had to be abandoned due to the difficulties of finding suitable animals. This resulted in the adoption of bays, but it was still stipulated by the brewers that all horses supplied to them by the breeders should weigh about 20 cwt and be not far short of 18 hands in height. Towards the end of 1973 Watney's last remaining working horses were retired, and the six bay Shires retained for showing left London in May 1973 for stables at West Bergholt, Essex, where they share facilities with Truman's (another well-known London brewery) five Suffolks, which have been stabled there for several years. In March 1973 the Watney Mann Shires won first prize in the team event at the Shire Horse Society's show at Peterborough.

Without doubt one of the most impressive turnouts at shows in recent years has been the magnificent eight-horse team (said to be the only one in this country) of black Shire geldings and dray with 16 beer casks on board, proudly owned and displayed by Young's of Wandsworth. On other occasions they have exhibited six-horse turnouts, with or without a ram in the cart behind the Shires – a ram being the symbol of the brewery. The same firm regularly enter their Shires for the Greater London Council's three-day horse show on Clapham Common, London. The grooming of horses at these events often includes drying their white feathers with very fine sawdust, after washing their legs, to accentuate the long hair on the fetlocks – in

Bob, *an 18.3 hands roan gelding bought in 1962 as a five-year-old by the Hull Brewery Co. Ltd.* Hull Brewery Co. Ltd

striking contrast to the blackness of the rest of the horse.

Yet another major brewery to favour the Shire is Courage Ltd, whose chairman, Mr R. H. Courage, is in fact president of the Shire Horse Society. Although no longer employing horses for the delivery of beer, the company continues to compete at shows throughout the country, including the heavy horse event at the Horse of the Year Show, which they have entered for the past 22 years. Courage's must be congratulated on building the Courage Shire Horse Centre at Maidenhead Thicket, about two miles west of Maidenhead in Berkshire. The impressive new stable block includes a blacksmith's shop, a coach house for the drays, and a foaling box. Another part of the complex contains the harness worn by the horses, together with the hundreds of prizes which Courage's Shires have won at shows over the years. The company hope to include examples of blacksmith's ironwork and of cooperage at a later date. Courage's ten Shires were moved to their new

An unusual view of a brewer's dray at the Easter Monday Van Horse Parade, Regent's Park.
Pamela Harrison

stables early in 1974, and the company hope that the Centre and the nearby Shire Horse Inn will become a place of interest to both British and foreign visitors, where they can visit and observe at close quarters Shire horses in the natural surroundings of the countryside.

With Shires dominating the London brewery scene in more recent years, it has been left to the Sunderland brewers, Vaux and Associated Breweries Ltd, to champion the cause of the immensely strong yet gentle Percheron. Like Whitbread's Shires, the Percherons start their working life at the age of four, and are generally in harness for the next ten years, although some of the horses continue with the brewery until they are 16 or 17 years old. Major A. R. A. Wilson, stable manager at Sunderland, has a very high regard for the Percheron, and is convinced, following 40 years' experience with heavy horses, that the Percheron is 'the almost perfect horse for the commercial stable of the present day'. The Vaux Percherons on average transport two loads a day within a radius of five miles from the brewery, and are also entered in turnout classes at numerous shows.

In a typical working day at the Vaux Sunderland stables, the horses are fed at 6.30 a.m., the stables are mucked out and a further feed given at 8 a.m., followed by harness-up and departure on a delivery round at 9 a.m. Between noon and 1 p.m. the horses return to the stables for their mid-day feed, leaving again soon after 1 p.m. for further deliveries until about 4.30 p.m. when the horses are dressed down, bedded, and given feed and hay. On

Lord Mais, a former Lord Mayor of London, with two fine Shire geldings, Shield and Armour, at Whitbread's City stables.
Daily Telegraph

Two of Whitbread's splendid Shires on beer delivery service in the heart of London. Whitbread & Co. Ltd

Saturdays the horses are extensively groomed between 8 and 11 a.m., and on Sundays they enjoy a full day of complete rest with beds down all day. The daily feeds consist of oats and bran, and a bran mash of either linseed or Epsom salts is given on Wednesdays and Saturdays. The average amount of hay and straw required each week by each horse is 2 cwt of straw and between 112 and 120 lbs of hay.

Another northern brewery to employ horses for local deliveries is Daniel Thwaites and Co. Ltd of the Star Brewery, Blackburn. This company started using Shires again in 1960 after a period of some 33 years. The first casks of beer brewed by Thwaites at Blackburn in 1807 were delivered on drays pulled by Shire horses. Today, 170 years later, the company's dray horses are still a colourful and familiar sight in the town, as the brewery consider that Shires still have a place in the commercial life of the company. With facilities to stable ten horses the brewery now keep seven Shires for delivering beer within one and a half miles of the brewery, operating five days a week.

The working day commences at about 7 a.m., when the horses are given a feed of bran and chopped hay, after which they are fitted out with harness and hitched up to their drays, either singly or in pairs. At the nearby loading yard, each vehicle is loaded with six 36-gallon casks – each team of Shires

Two of James Buchanan's Clydesdales at the Glasgow docks collecting cask staves for the firm's cooperage. James Buchanan & Co. Ltd

delivers between three and four tons a day. About noon the horses return to the stables for feeding, after which further deliveries continue until approximately 4.30 p.m. Sharp stones, glass and sometimes metal present a constant hazard to the horses' feet, which are examined every night to ensure that nothing has been picked up that might cause pain or injury. A further meal of bran and chop is given to the horses before they are bedded down on clean straw, fresh wood shavings, and soft peat moss. A final feed is given about 9 p.m., when a stableman checks to see that all is well for the night.

A local blacksmith renews shoes every five or six weeks, when light grass plates are fitted. However, when the horses are to be exhibited at a show, eight-pound wrought iron bevel-edged shoes are fitted, which are often as much as eleven inches across. The Thwaites Shires are bought at four years of age and, if possible, from breeders in Derbyshire or Lincolnshire. They are worked and shown for an average period of 14 years. Every horse in the Star Brewery stable is given a three-week holiday in the country during the summer months – normally in the tree-shaded meadows on the southern slopes of the Ribble valley not far from Blackburn.

On the showground the horses pull 12-cwt red and gold four-wheeled drays, which are loaded with three casks of two 36-gallon barrels and a

Four of Whitbread's Shires –
Armour, Gilbert II, Sullivan *and*
Shield – *kick the city dust off their*
heels in rural Kent. Daily Telegraph

Courage's Shires pulling a dray.
Courage Ltd

kilderkin with a capacity of 18 gallons, plus crates of bottled beer. Two types of vehicle are used – the Lancashire dray, which has an open body, and the London van dray with low sides to the body and large five-foot diameter rear wheels. In both instances the driver controls his team of Shires from a seat about eight feet above ground level, and for safety is strapped in as a sharp jolt could easily throw him to the ground when the horses are travelling at a fast trot or have reached a full gallop. The stable show gear is valued at several thousand pounds. The black leather harness, strengthened in places with steel, is decorated with gleaming brass fittings, including the company's star symbol on the collar. Brass beer casks ornament the blinkers and the saddle, and each horse has its name rivetted to the front of its collar. The drivers wear livery of brown jackets with red facings, cavalry twill knee breeches, brown boots and leggings. Grey bowlers and red ties complete the elegant sartorial appearance of the horsemen.

Taking pride of place in the Thwaites stable is *Drayman*, a black Shire gelding, which won over 50 prizes during the first three years he was exhibited. *Drayman*, Northamptonshire-born in 1956, has taken part in the Horse of the Year Show in London, and in 1963 won the heavy horse single turnout championship at the National Heavy Horse Show at Peterborough. Later in the year, after competing at the Royal Show, he was selected to appear on television as a typical example of a pure-bred English Shire horse. After collecting a third prize for harnessed pairs with their black geldings at the 1974 National Shire Horse Show at Peterborough, Thwaites did very well at the Royal Lancashire Agricultural Society Show at Ribby Hall, where they picked up three firsts in the harnessed pairs, yoked and team classes.

Without being over-sentimental – and what company can afford to be that today – it is heartening to learn how many of the senior directors of the

Sullivan, *a dapple-grey Shire gelding, overjoyed with his new-found freedom at the start of his summer holiday on the Whitbread hop farm at Beltring in Kent.*
Daily Telegraph

largest British breweries are sincerely dedicated to the preservation and promotion of the heavy horse. Major R. W. Gleadow, former chairman and managing director of the Hull Brewery Co. Ltd, has even compiled a fascinating little booklet called *Hull Brewery Horses*. This brewery, situated on the northern bank of the River Humber, employed horses for more than 70 years, and only stopped using them for delivery work in 1973. Horses are still kept for show purposes.

Although 1890s-period photographs are in existence, the earliest actual records of the Hull Brewery horses start in 1909 when a horse called *Major* was purchased for £60. Ten times this figure is now being paid for the best geldings. Between 1909 and 1970 the brewery purchased a total of 45 horses. It is sad to note that two suffered tragic deaths – one the result of a head-on collision with a car, and the other incurring strangulation and a broken neck after catching a crib-chain between foot and shoe during the night. Another fine horse had to be destroyed because of a brain tumour. On a lighter note, *Royal* was sold to a farmer after only one year because of 'spring itch', and *Scalby Lady* was also sold because she became unreasonably irritable in heavy rain. During World War I four horses from the brewery were requisitioned for service with the army overseas, where they pulled gun carriages and transported supplies.

In 1956 the company purchased *Prince*, a five-year-old bay Clydesdale gelding, for the sum of £180. Shortly before his retirement at the age of 19, this fine 17.2 hands animal was invited to attend the 1970 Horse of the Year Show at Earls Court, London, to appear in the parade of personalities. The brewery estimate that in a working life of 14 years this grand old horse had covered more than 15,000 miles and transported over 10,000 tons of beer. The Hull Brewery entered their seven-year-old dark bay gelding *Noble* for three classes at the 1974 National Shire Horse Show, where he won the four-year-old gelding class and was reserve to the champion gelding of the show, thus following in the footsteps of his prize-winning predecessors who, in 1970 alone, collected five magnificent cups and 26 rosettes at numerous shows.

Just as at least a dozen English breweries have, in recent years, used heavy horses for delivering beer, it is perhaps equally appropriate that these splendid animals should also be associated with that other beverage that is held in such high esteem north of the border. James Buchanan and Co. Ltd, the distillers of Black and White, Buchanan's and Strathconan Scotch whiskies, still stable heavy horses for work and show purposes. Forty years ago the company employed as many as 45 horses for delivery work within the city of Glasgow. By the 1950s, this number was reduced to 20, and today only six horses are kept at the Warroch Street stables. Five of these horses are used for transporting cask staves from storage at the docks to the firm's cooperage, a distance of about half a mile each day. In addition, at certain peak periods of the year, whisky is delivered to establishments in the centre of the city. Appropriately, two of the present horses are Clydesdales, one bay and the other blue roan, and the other four are, even more fittingly, black and white Clydesdale – Shire cross geldings, between 17 and 18 hands in height. During the summer months the horses compete at numerous shows within a 60-mile radius of Glasgow. The company's horses won 13 cups and a total of nearly 60 prizes in the shows attended in 1974. As with the English breweries, this record reflects great credit on the distillers.

10.
The Future
of the Heavy Horse

*Geoffrey Morton with a Shire mare and her foal on
his East Yorkshire farm.* Thames Television

What, many people ask, is the ultimate future of the heavy horse in Britain? It would be both injudicious and presumptuous to make a categorical prophecy for even ten years' time. However, at the time of writing the portents are favourable.

One of the most reliable indicators to the future must be the state of the four main breed societies. Fortunately they are still enthusiastically dedicated to the prolongation and promotion of the breeds that bear their name, with no lowering of the high standards set and maintained over the years since the distinctive breeds were established and the respective societies were formed.

Mr Roy Bird, the indefatigable secretary of the Shire Horse Society, confirms that the total membership is now over the 1,000 mark, and that during the past five years or so more than 500 new members have joined the society. The Shire Horse Society has trebled the number of stud book registrations compared with 1964, when the demand for the heavy type of draft horse was at an extremely low ebb, and prices at rock bottom. The parent society has eight area stallion hiring societies throughout Britain. Each of these district branches hires out a stallion every year, which may either travel the area or be available at a member's farm for stud purposes. The demand for Shires in Britain and abroad is now higher than it has been been since 1945.

About 3,000 visitors attended the 1974 British Percheron Society's show. Membership of this much more recent society is approaching the 100 figure, and is on the increase, with about 100 registered mares in the stud book. The society states that new studs have been started, and to meet the increased demand for Percherons additional breeding stock has been imported from France during the last few years.

Membership of the Suffolk Horse Society is also on the increase, with approximately 350 members and about 50 Suffolk breeders in Britain in 1974. A few horses of this breed continue to be exported to the USA and the Argentine, and 100 mares are registered in the society stud book.

Another positive pointer to the present much more healthy heavy horse situation is the increased membership of the various horse ploughing associations, and the fact that the number of teams competing at the many ploughing matches held between April and November steadily increases year by year. Some of these ploughing matches are attended by as many as 2,000 keenly interested and knowledgeable people of all ages, who often travel many miles to watch the now rare skill of horse and ploughman. The Southern Counties Heavy Horse Association (originally known as the Southern Counties Horse Ploughing Association) has built up a membership of over 500 during its first three years, and members of the association show their own horses in nearly a dozen counties, from Suffolk on the east coast to Dorset in the south-west. Approximately 30 members employ their heavy horses to a greater or lesser degree on their farms, nurseries and smallholdings. Over 5,000 visitors attended the association's 1974 Spring Working near Billingshurst, Sussex.

Almost all pursuits, whether for pleasure or profit, require a certain degree of skill and experience to perform them well. At the same time the onlooker, unless he or she has been initiated into a craft like ploughing, finds it very difficult to appreciate the amount of skill required by the ploughman to control both horse and plough with precision. Therefore a slight digression

84

A two-horse team ploughing on a farm in Cumbria. Tom Parker

into the basics of ploughing may be helpful at this point.

To the uninitiated, ploughing a straight furrow across a field and then tilling the soil looks a deceptively simple and automatic operation. In reality, ploughing involves a number of variations and far-from-simple movements by both horse and ploughman. In ploughing matches it is not only necessary to draw a single straight furrow of a predetermined length on a meadow loaned by a farmer, but an area of about 700 square yards must be ploughed as well. These rectangular areas, which may be some 80 yards in length, have an 'opening' at one of the ends and this is where the ploughing starts. Judges at these matches, after observing the straightness of the furrow, will also pay attention to the 'crown', which consists of three or more furrows on either side of the opening; the strip or slice of soil that has been transferred by the plough; the 'ins and outs', which are the places at which the plough penetrates and is withdrawn from the soil at the end of the furrows; the troughs or seams between the slices of soil; and the firmness and seed bed.

The share is the blade of the plough that cuts horizontally at the base of the furrow, while the coulter makes a vertical incision in the soil, producing the furrow slice or strip which is then inverted by the mouldboard. The mouldboard is a curved metal plate behind the share: it turns the cut furrow slice into a long strip of soil, so covering all the unwanted surface weeds and stubble.

Different classes involving the various styles of ploughing are usually arranged by the organizers of matches. These variations may include 'high cut', when the furrow slice is cut at a sharper angle and may be as high as it is wide; 'long and short turn-furrows', which are dependent upon the mouldboard; and 'reversible ploughing'. The condition of the soil and the seeds to be sown determine the type of ploughing chosen.

With prices of £600–700 being paid for large, four-year-old geldings, breeders are again being suitably rewarded and materially encouraged for their perseverance and years of selective breeding. As mentioned earlier,

A three-horse team harrowing on Bela Camp Farm, Cumbria. Tom Parker

considerably higher prices are now being paid for top-class stallions and brood mares than previously. These vastly experienced breeders are quite indispensable to the continuance of showing, promotion, sale and employment for agriculture and commercial work, in Britain and abroad, of the four main breeds of heavy horse. It is also gratifying to learn that two of the breed societies have about 100 brood mares registered in their stud books. There are also approximately 170 breeders recognized by the three English-domiciled societies.

A number of breeders combine farming with rearing pure-bred heavy horses, more often than not employing horses for cultivating their land. Mr R. J. Brickell, who manages the Witney Stud at Enstone, Oxfordshire home of those two fine stallions *Lymm Sovereign* and *Cotswold Grey King,* uses his horses for work on the Drystone Hill Estate. This successful breeder of Shires keeps two stallions at stud, and has had almost 30 mares in foal at one time. Registered colts, fillies and mature horses are always available; and several animals are exported each year to Canada and the USA. Visitors are always made very welcome at this stud, but out of courtesy an appointment should be arranged first. Another well-known and successful breeder of Shires is Mr R. Hull, who runs the Stanley House Stud at St Michael's-on-Wyre, Preston, Lancashire. One of his finest stallions over the last ten years is *Stanley House Black Prince,* foaled in 1966, by *His Excellency,* a champion of many shows in the late 1950s and bred by another outstanding breeder of Shires, the late Mr J. Gould of Lymm. Yet another descendant of the renowned Lymm Shires is a grey stallion, *Stanley House Grey King,* owned by Mr Bourne and at stud at his Brenchley Shire Stud at Palmers Green, Kent.

Among those who steadfastly continue to employ heavy horses on their farms is Mr Geoffrey Morton, who farms about 130 acres of arable land at Nod, near Holme-upon-Spalding Moor, without a tractor or any other form of motorized machinery. This East Yorkshire farmer maintains with deep

*Open Day at the Courage Shire
Horse Centre, Maidenhead, for
members of the Shire Horse Society.*
Courage Ltd

conviction that horses provide a better way of farming, and one which may
well become more attractive to farmers of the future – particularly if the price
of oil continues to rise. The more that fuel costs escalate, the greater the
financial gain achieved by employing horses on the land. To keep a reasonable
number of working horses on his farm, Mr Morton breeds his own
replacements, preferring to pay, when necessary, a relatively small stud fee
for a visiting stallion as opposed to paying between £300–400 for a fully-
grown adult horse. Each year, Mr Morton attends the Shire horse show held
at Peterborough, where other breeders and members of the Shire Horse
Society meet to discuss the future of the heavy horse in agriculture and
commerce. Mr Morton's particular interest lies in judging stallions – any
one of these magnificent Shires may be of sufficient merit to be a suitable
sire for a foal to be born the following year. Two foals are normally born
each year on Mr Morton's farm, following the visit to his farm by a stallion
of his choice to 'cover' his mares. The young horses are broken at two years,
used for full working duties when three-year-olds, and remain in harness
until they are about 20. One remarkable mare for which Mr Morton has a
special affection is *Violet*, aged 27. She was one of the first horses ever
purchased by Mr Morton, who has employed her for full working duties and
as a brood mare. She has produced a number of fine foals over the years.
Now she spends most of her time peacefully grazing in one of the meadows,

Geoffrey Morton and two of his beloved Shires. Thames Television

only occasionally undertaking a little light work when extra help is required at peak periods.

Being an arable farmer, Mr Morton is able to provide the oats, hay and turnips from his own land as winter and supplementary summer feed when grazing is minimal. The cost of new shoes every two or three months is a constant, budgetable factor, far more agreeable than the unpredictable and often expensive repair costs following the purchase of a second-hand tractor costing several hundred pounds. Following the making of a television documentary about Mr Morton and his farming methods (*Pride of Place,* made by Tyne Tees Television as part of their *About Britain* series), a second film was made, showing one man's affection for his Shire horses and their everyday employment on his Yorkshire farm. Although Mr Morton also keeps store pigs and has a few chickens, his farm is dominated by his splendid Shires. The film showed the deep understanding, rapport and respect that Mr Morton has for his horses and for nature. He must be admired for his fierce independence and stubborn refusal to yield to mechanization. The film's director, too, deserves credit for his patient, sympathetic treatment of this subject of one man and his horses, and for committing to film a traditional way of life which only a few years ago was threatened with extinction.

Another farmer who shares many of Mr Morton's views is Mr Percy Howe of Brook Farm, near Wellington, Somerset, who at the time of the 1973 fuel

Running repairs on the spot – the farrier visits the farm. W. Wilkinson

crisis reverted to Shire horses. His decision to return to horses was not only influenced by the rising cost of oil and tractor upkeep, but 'because horses are able to work land unsuitable for tractors, horses are better company, and the enforced walking keeps me fit'. A Surrey company of market gardeners, who specialize in growing trees and shrubs, still employ cross-bred Shires, claiming that when used for hoeing between the shrubs horses are more economical and quicker than the less manoeuvrable tractor. Daily rations for these working horses generally consist of about 5–6 lbs of dry oats, chaff, between 10 and 12 lbs of hay, plus potatoes and treacle.

Fortunately for those who not only admire the noble, gentle strength of these sublime animals with their glossy coats rippling with muscle, but who also respect the traditional way of life, there are still a number of dedicated men who combine the basic, time-honoured skills of horse breeding and farming. One knowledgeable exponent of these complementary crafts is Mr Nick Rayner who farms at Wootton, near New Milton on the edge of the New Forest in Hampshire. Confirming the reference in Chapter 1 to the

Mr Cyril Sissons of Beswick driving spokes of a wagon wheel into an elm hub. Roy Shaw

usefulness of horses in situations where tractors cannot be used, Mr Rayner says there are numerous occasions when his land is much too wet for a tractor to be used, and here the horse comes into its own, having a considerably less damaging effect on the soil. Both Mr Rayner and Mr R. J. Brickell of the Witney Stud at Enstone are in agreement that, while horses can be bred and bought, the major inhibiting factor restricting the widespread use of heavy horses in agriculture at the present time is the difficulty in obtaining new horse ploughs, and to a lesser extent replacement harness, as there are so few firms manufacturing this type of agricultural equipment. Many farmers who are determined to continue cultivating their land with horses have, like Geoffrey Morton, been forced to purchase horse ploughing equipment from suppliers in America. It is, however, very heartening to learn that in this technological age there are still craftsmen like Mr Cyril Sissons who, with loving and patient care, restore the old, traditional farm wagons and carts. The Sissons family of Beswick, a small village between Beverley and Great Driffield in East Yorkshire, have practised the wheelwright's skills for over

Two Shires in the paddock at the Courage Shire Horse Centre, Maidenhead, with the stable complex in the background. Courage Ltd

100 years. Initially, when horses dominated agricultural life, the wheelwright's work was almost exclusively concerned with constructing wheels and farm carts. Today, he has to undertake work of a more general nature to remain in business, and to be available for those who are fortunate enough to own or unearth one of the traditional carts of the past. Occasionally the firm are asked to build a replica of one of the old-type horse-drawn wagons, which they do with a rare knowledge and pride.

The very significant and admirable contribution made by many of the breweries, both large and small, has already been covered in Chapter 9. However, it is of interest to note that management consultants to the industry have in recent years studied the economics of horse-drawn transportation very carefully. Their cost analysis has led to the conclusion that delivery of beer by horse-drawn vehicles is a cheaper proposition than by petrol- or diesel-engined lorries over short distances up to about two miles, in congested, built-up areas, involving a good deal of stopping and starting. With the ever-increasing cost of fuel and of new vehicles, this estimated distance of two miles from the brewery will probably increase. Additional operating factors include the cost of repairs compared with occasional veterinary charges to keep the horses in a good state of health. The cost of a replacement horse and that of bought-in feed must remain considerably less than the combined cost of a new lorry and the fuel consumed over the years it is in operation.

Although the export of the heavy type of draft horse is no longer a major British industry, the continued interest abroad in the main breeds does influence their revival in this country. It is, therefore, extremely encouraging to learn from the publicity director of the American Shire Horse Society that there has been a tremendous revival of interest in draft horses in the USA. It is estimated that between 40 and 50 Shires have been imported from Britain during the past five or six years, and this despite the fact that the cost of importation from abroad is too high for most breeders and farmers. It is thought that the future emphasis will be on expansion by American breeders, but if present trends continue, it will be some years before they can meet the demand in their own country. It would therefore seem the ideal time for breeders in the British Isles to export horses to the USA, before

American breeders are able to supply all the draft horses needed in their own country – the only major hurdle being high transportation costs, whether by air or sea.

Confining their observations to the state of Maryland, the Maryland Shire Horse Associates report that over the last seven years there has been a 'phenomenal growth of interest in the Shire breed of horses'. Mr Emerald Busse, a noted Illinois breeder of Clydesdales, advises that the demand for heavy horses in America has never been better than it is now, in the mid-1970s. At the beginning of 1974 Mr Busse had 25 Clydesdales for immediate sale, and was also in a position to supply wagons, carts and other horse-drawn equipment at his stud.

On a less happy note, the continental demand for horsemeat may well act as a counter to the undoubted revival of the main breeds in Britain. Since World War II many hundreds of horses (but not only heavy draft horses) from the British Isles have been slaughtered or transported alive to the continent, where they have been purchased by large meat wholesalers for restaurants and small butchers. Unfortunately there are facilities in Britain for both the large-scale slaughtering and deep-freeze storage of carcases prior to shipment abroad, mostly in refrigerated cargo boats. Should an appreciable number of pedigree horses, either mares or stallions in their prime, or worse still just approaching maturity, be sold, albeit unwittingly, for instant slaughter or shipment abroad, it could well have an adverse effect on British breeding stock. Fortunately the vast majority of breeders are acutely aware of the dangers and in any case deplore the slaughter of any type of horse for human consumption.

There is no room for even the smallest degree of complacency. It is essential that the four breed societies continue to encourage new membership, the breeding and promotion of their individual breeds in this country and abroad, and continue the addition of stallion premiums to those granted by the Horserace Betting Levy Board. Continued sponsorship by banks, breweries and other commercial organizations at horse shows and ploughing matches is vital. With Britain still in the Common Market, increased vigilance is necessary concerning the export of horses to the continent for human consumption.

As far as the employment of heavy horses on farms is concerned, there are two very important aspects worthy of consideration by the breed societies and others. One is that a serious effort should be made either to locate or, if necessary, establish a small engineering company specializing in the manufacture and renovation of horse-orientated agricultural implements, from harness to ploughs. Such a firm could expect financial support from all breeders, since it would ensure that any farmer proposing to use heavy horses on his land would not be deterred by the lack of suitable equipment.

A second, equally important development would be the inclusion at agricultural colleges and similar establishments of a short course on horse management and the use of farm implements designed for cultivation by horses as opposed to tractors. Valuable advice could be obtained from breeders and members of the horse ploughing societies, who could not only recommend a suitable syllabus, but might be approached to lecture on their respective subjects. This would ensure that future generations of farmers would at least have the opportunity of learning how to manage and employ on the farm that noble and hard-working animal, the British heavy horse.

11. Glossary of Terms

Bay Reddish brown colour – most bays generally have a darker mane and tail.

Blaze White marking on forehead – also referred to as a *star*.

Blinkers Part of the bridle, worn to protect or shield the eyes.

Breast Collar As opposed to the more usual neck collar, the breast type of collar encircles the chest, being more of a band than a collar, and is only used for light work.

Breechings Part of the harness, located over the back and hindquarters, and used when the horse is between the shafts of a cart.

Bridle The head harness by which the horse is controlled.

Brood Mare Female horse used for breeding.

Chesnut (Not spelt chestnut) – light reddish-brown colour, which in the case of the Suffolk may be one of seven shades.

Clean Leg One without an excess of long hair or feather from below the knee.

Colt Young horse, generally accepted as a male, before either being gelded or maturing into an adult stallion.

Coulter Part of the plough which makes a vertical incision in the soil.

Crest Upper curve of the neck.

Crown Three or more furrows made by the plough at the start of a ploughing match.

Crupper Part of the breechings harness – a strap which lies along the horse's back behind the saddle.

Dapple-grey Often associated with Percherons, and generally denotes small patches of darker and lighter grey hair.

Entire Used to describe an ungelded male horse.

Feather Long, silky hair below the knee, mostly covering the fetlock. A characteristic of the earlier Shire.

Fetlock The lower part of the leg above the hoof.

Filly Young female horse – young female foal.

Fly-Terrets Harness decoration attached to the head strap behind the ears.

Foal Young horse of either sex.

Furrow Groove or trench made by the plough in the soil.

Furrow Slice Strip or slice of soil that has been cut and transferred by the plough.

Gelding Castrated male horse.

Girth Measurement around the centre of the back; also the band round the body attached to the saddle.

Grease Ailment of the leg, affecting the heel; more prevalent in horses with an abundance of hair on the lower part of the leg.

Grey In addition to obvious shades of dark to light grey, grey is also used to refer to almost pure white horses. (A pure white horse would be an albino.)

Hames Part of the neck collar – two open prongs which project upwards in front of the withers, and incorporating attachments (hooks or rings) to which the trace chains are fastened. Also known as *tees*.

Hand Measurement indicating the height of a horse. One hand is four inches.

Height Measured in hands from the ground to the top of the withers.

High-Cut Ploughing term relating to a class or style of ploughing – the furrow slice or strip is cut at a sharper angle and may be as high as it is wide.

Hock The joint on the hind leg, between the knee and the fetlock.

Housen Part of the harness, located behind the upper part of the collar and fastened to the hames; it protects the upper part of the horse and the rest of the harness.

In Hand Showing class for horses when they are paraded without harness or vehicle, and led by a halter only before the judges.

Ins and Outs Ploughing term for the places at which the plough penetrates and is withdrawn from the soil at the end of a furrow.

Martingale Strap positioned between the front legs and attached to the collar at one end and the girth at the other.

Mouldboard Curved metal plate located behind the share on the plough, which turns the cut furrow slice into a long strip of soil.

Pastern The front part of the horse's foot.

Roman Nose Aquiline, curved nose, sometimes seen on the Shire.

Share Part of the plough that cuts horizontally at the base of the furrow.

Sidebone Ossification of the cartilage in the foot.

Stallion Adult male horse, entire and ungelded.

Star See *Blaze*.

Stud Establishment where horses are bred, and where both thoroughbred stallions and brood mares are kept.

Stud Book Record book of thoroughbreds.

Tandem Formation of two or more horses hitched in front of each other, nose to tail.

Tees See *Hames*.

Thoroughbred Horse whose sire and dam are both recorded in the stud book of that particular breed – a horse of pure blood.

Top Latch Leather strap which secures the tops of the hames together.

Traces Chains or leather side straps attached to the collar hame mountings.

Whipple-Tree Horizontal bar suspended behind the horse when working on the farm; it ensures that the traces are kept away from the horse's side while it is working.

Withers Located at the base of the upper part of the neck where the back starts. See *Height*.